RAYS' AWAR

RAYS' AWARENESS

Radiation Health Effects

Made Easy

with

Professor Dee and Doctor Hay

To Sandy
with best wishes

Ken Chadwick

Whis & Co

© K H Chadwick, 2014

Published by Whis & Co

A CIP catalogue record for this book is available from the British Library.

ISBN 978-0-9931158-0-6

Book layout and cover design by Clare Brayshaw

Prepared and printed by:
York Publishing Services Ltd
64 Hallfield Road
Layerthorpe
York YO31 7ZQ

Tel: 01904 431213

Website: www.yps-publishing.co.uk

For

Hilary, Carolyn, Victoria and Bonnie,

the ladies in my life.

Much have I travell'd in the realms of gold,
And many goodly states and kingdoms seen;
Round many western islands have I been
Which bards in fealty to Apollo hold.
Oft of one wide expanse had I been told
That deep-brow'd Homer rules as his demesne;
Yet did I never breathe its pure serene
Till I heard Chapman speak out loud and bold:
Then felt I like some watcher of the skies
When a new planet swims into his ken;
Or like stout Cortez when with eagle eyes
He star'd at the Pacific – and all his men
Look'd at each other with a wild surmise –
Silent, upon a peak in Darien.

John Keats (1795-1821)
"On First Looking into Chapman's Homer"

"Only connect…"

EM Forster (1879-1970)
"Howards End"

About the author

Ken Chadwick, PhD, was born in Darwen, Lancashire and studied physics and radiation biophysics in Liverpool and London in England and Utrecht in The Netherlands. He is a Fellow of the Institute of Physics and the Society for Radiological Protection, both in the UK. He spent 20 years in The Netherlands and 15 years in Belgium working in the Radiation Protection Research Programme of the European Commission, first doing research and then managing European research contracts on radiation biology and health effects. He is a co-author of over 140 articles and 9 books in the scientific literature and served 10 years on the editorial board of the Journal of Radiological Protection. He now divides his time between the English Lake District and a Greek island.

Preface

After some 40 years developing an interpretation of radiation biological effects with a colleague (Dr H P Leenhouts), I felt it might be useful to present our interpretation in a simple way to make it accessible to a wider audience. The disaster at Fukushima in 2011, the sensational reporting of it and the panic reaction to it by the local population, convinced me that a popular science book was necessary to describe radiation and radioactivity and explain how I think radiation affects us.

So, I have conscripted a couple of fictitious friends, Professor Dee and Doctor Hay, to guide you, the reader, through the puzzle. If you have the patience to put all the pieces of the puzzle together, you will gain a clear insight into how radiation causes its damaging health effects. Although the interpretation is not proven, it is supported by a large amount of experimental data; it is largely intuitive and it works. My conviction is that by understanding radiation and its health effects we can learn to live with it without fear.

This book would not have been written without the suggestion, prodding and encouragement of my two daughters, Victoria and Carolyn, and it is a pleasure to acknowledge their role in getting the book started. They are not particularly good at maths but the introduction of a few simple equations in the text proved to be unavoidable. I hope that they, like you, will understand the main thrust of the book.

I have also to acknowledge the patient, expert help that I got from my dear wife, Hilary, who converted my long and verbose sentences into a more flowing and logical text. Hilary also made the suggestion that Professor Dee and Doctor Hay's interjections would liven up the more stolid sections.

Bonnie, our lovely Bichon Frisé, has been a constant companion at the computer throughout the whole gestation of the book, prompting me when we needed to take a break.

And finally, I have to say that without the 40 years of friendly, cooperative research with Henk Leenhouts, the concepts, analyses and understanding of radiation action presented here would never have been possible.

Ken Chadwick
Kendal
June 2014

Contents

CHAPTER 1

Radiation, Radioactivity and DNA

1.1 Introduction

The word "radiation" conjures up a sense of fear in most of us. It is a fear which arises from an inability to "feel" or "see" radiation and a general lack of knowledge about the biological and health effects that radiation is known to cause. In addition, radiation is often associated with the devastation and enormous loss of life caused by the atomic bombs dropped at Hiroshima and Nagasaki in 1945.

Prof Dee and Dr Hay's Take Home Message is:

There is no need to fear radiation and we hope to prove that to you. However, we do have to treat it with a great deal of respect.

Actually, the health effects of radiation can be conveniently divided into three parts: short-term effects, cancer and hereditary effects.

Short-term effects, such as skin burns, radiation sickness, organ damage or failure, vomiting, anaemia and ultimately death, will usually reveal themselves a few days to a couple of weeks after exposure to substantial amounts of radiation.

Cancer might arise as a consequence of any exposure to radiation although, the lower the exposure, the lower the chance of getting cancer. It is an effect of radiation which might occur many years after exposure and, unless the exposure is to a specific organ and quite large, it will be very difficult to be sure that the cancer was, in fact, caused by radiation. It is, for example, certain that the thyroid cancers found in young children living close to Chernobyl, a few years after the 1986 reactor accident, were the result of exposure to high levels of radioactive iodine released in the reactor fire. On the other hand, it is not normally appreciated that an intensive follow-up of the atomic bomb survivors in Japan shows that up to the end of 2003 about 40% of the survivors were still alive. The follow-up also shows that only about 5% of some 11,000 cancer deaths found in the survivors can be directly ascribed to their radiation exposure.

Hereditary effects might arise in the next or subsequent generations of radiation-exposed people as a consequence of changes induced in the reproductive cells. These sorts of effects of radiation have been demonstrated in fruit flies and in mice but, so far, there is no definite indication of this sort of effect in man. Hereditary effects have not yet been recorded in the offspring of the atomic bomb survivors. However, there is no doubt that exposure of the reproductive organs to large amounts of radiation can cause sterility.

Over the past 40 years, a very simple and straightforward way of interpreting radiation effects has been developed. This interpretation provides a quantitative analysis and a descriptive appreciation of how radiation affects the cells of the body and how this leads to the three biological consequences just described. It offers a wide and visually intuitive understanding of radiation action at the molecular level and gives clear insights into the health risks of radiation. This interpretation, called a model, is in harmony with a great body of experimental data but it challenges older and more widely accepted radiation biological dogma. Consequently, it is not recognised by all radiation scientists. However, it works and so, with the resurgence of interest in the development of nuclear power to satisfy the need for energy and the concomittant nervousness in the general public about its safety, especially after the Chernobyl accident and the earthquake and tsunami at Fukushima in Japan in 2011, it was felt that a popular science book explaining these ideas about radiation effects and risks might be useful.

In order for you, the reader, to be able to follow and understand this explanation of radiation action, you will need to learn a bit about radiation and a bit about DNA and its role in the cells of the body. You will also encounter a few, very simple, mathematical equations, for that is all it takes to quantify the radiation effects, although you do not need to understand all of the equations. With these bits of knowledge, you will be able to get insights into radiation effects and understand radiation risks.

Only the terms needed to make things understandable are defined and used and the reasoning is not taken to any greater depth than is necessary. Those of you with a scientific background will have to excuse anything that appears to be incomplete or superficial but this book is also intended for those who do not have any scientific training. If mathematical equations bother you, then you should ignore them but try to follow their graphical representations. The equations are included so that those who can understand them can appreciate the reasoning quantitatively as well as qualitatively.

The aim of this book is to help you to appreciate the dangers of radiation from a rational point of view and to realise that, when treated with respect, radiation does not have to be feared.

Dr Hay and Prof Dee's Take Home Message is:

Put together a few bits of information about radiation, cells and DNA with a simple model and you can understand how radiation affects us.

1.2   Radiation and Radioactivity

"Radiation" and "Radioactivity" are very frequently and frustratingly confused with each other, especially in the popular press, so the first thing that needs to be done is to separate the one from the other.

Starting with "radioactivity", any material that emits atomic radiation has some radioactivity in it. And that means that, because a small part of the potassium in your bodies is radioactive and emits rather energetic, penetrating radiation, you are all a little bit radioactive! It isn't enough to make you ill but you are all emitting it continuously. The radiation emitted by a radioactive material cannot be "switched off".

"Radiation" is emitted by material which is radioactive. However, radiation is not the same as radioactivity and can never be radioactive. This is one confusing mistake often perpetrated by the media. Radiation is also created and emitted by X-ray machines and 'particle' accelerators and this radiation can be switched off by switching the machine or accelerator off.

The different radiations can be divided up into alpha (α), beta (β) and gamma (γ) radiations, named after the first three letters of the Greek alphabet, X-rays which most of you will have heard of, and 'fast' and 'thermal' neutrons. Although this isn't an all-inclusive listing, these are the important radiations which are discussed in more detail later.

Alpha, beta and gamma radiations are emitted by different radioactive materials, whereas X-rays are made by X-ray machines and neutrons arise in nuclear reactors. Alpha radiation is not very penetrating, is easily stopped by a piece of paper and is not a dangerous source of external exposure. Beta radiation is more penetrating than alpha radiation but can be stopped by a few millimeters of lead or a few centimeters of water or plastic. Gamma radiation is very penetrating and requires several centimeters of lead or a meter or two of concrete to stop it. X-rays are similar to gamma rays but are generally less energetic and therefore a little less penetrating. Neutrons are very penetrating but can be slowed down most effectively by water and then absorbed by special neutron absorbing materials, such as boron or cadmium.

Another frequent confusion with the terms "radiation" and "radioactivity" is the mistaken impression that something which has been "irradiated" must then become "radioactive". This does not happen. Single use disposable medical products, such as rubber gloves or surgical drapes, are sterilised by large doses of ionising radiation, often gamma rays, but do not become radioactive and are perfectly safe to handle. Food which is irradiated, to prevent sprouting in onions or to kill bacteria in chicken and shrimp, for example, is not radioactive after the treatment and is safe to eat. The tyres on your car which may be irradiated to stabilise the rubber are not radioactive either. And you, when you go to have your broken ankle X-rayed after a skiing accident, are not radioactive after the X-ray. In fact, the radiation leaves no trace and it is virtually impossible to detect whether something or someone has been irradiated.

The important exception to this is that things can be made radioactive when they absorb the slow or "thermal" neutrons. Great advantage is taken of this process and many different radioactive compounds are made in research nuclear reactors or at accelerators which are sources of the thermal neutrons. These radioactive compounds are used in hospitals for the diagnosis of specific illnesses.

Prof Dee and Dr Hay's Take Home Message is:

Radioactive materials emit radiation but radiation itself is never radioactive and irradiated materials are not made radioactive either.

1.3 Cells, Chromosomes and DNA

Human tissue is made up of millions of very small, more or less spherical cells which are a few microns, that is, a few thousandths of a millimeter, in diameter. A cell is made up of about 80% water and 20% more complex molecules, such as proteins, enzymes and sugars. Inside each cell is a liquid, the cytoplasm, and a nucleus that contains the genetic information which governs the activity of the cell. In the cell nucleus, the genetic material is the well-known DNA (**d**eoxyribo**n**ucleic **a**cid), the famous double helix molecule. In humans, the DNA is divided up into forty-six chromosomes. These forty-six chromosomes are actually twenty-three pairs of similar but not exactly identical chromosomes. You all received one of each pair of chromosomes from your mother and the other of each pair from your father.

Strangely, all the cells in your bodies carry exactly the same forty-six chromosomes even though some cells are blood cells, some are liver cells and some are brain cells. The cells of your body and the chromosomes in the cells can be seen using a normal microscope and the chromosomes have been given numbers from one, for the longest, to twenty-two, for the shortest. And you each have two chromosomes which determine your sex. If you are female, you have two X chromosomes, one from your mother and one from your father and if you are male, you have one X chromosome from your mother and one Y chromosome from your father.

One gram, a centimeter cube, of tissue contains about one billion cells and each cell carries in its nucleus some two meters of DNA which is a long, thread-like molecule, rather like a coiled-up rope ladder. The two meters of DNA are all folded up in the different chromosomes but, remarkably, all under control. You might wonder how all this DNA does not get tangled up but the molecules in the cell which check it, copy it and repair it, all manage to do that without getting it into knots. The DNA double helix carries the genetic code which determines how the cell functions in the body. The continuing integrity of the DNA molecules and, consequently, the chromosomes in the cell nucleus, is crucial to the normal ongoing function of the cell. The DNA is, therefore, an important target for radiation damage.

The model described in later chapters, which aims to allow you to understand how radiation affects you, is based quite simply on the damage which radiation does to the DNA double helix.

And the Take Home Message is:

Radiation damages the DNA in the nucleus of our cells and this damage causes the radiation health effects.

1.4 Basic Principles of Radiation Protection

There are three simple ways in which you can protect yourselves from an external radiation source:

1. **Minimise the time of exposure:** the biological effect of radiation is related to the total amount or "dose" of radiation you are exposed to, so the less time you are exposed, the lower the dose.

2. **Maximise the distance from the source of radiation:** the intensity of radiation from both a source of radioactivity and an X-ray machine decreases rapidly the further you are from the source, so you can reduce your exposure by moving away from the source as rapidly as possible.

3. **Maximise the amount of shielding between you and the source of radiation:** the intensity of radiation from a radioactive gamma ray source and an X-ray machine can be drastically reduced by imposing shielding in the form of a few centimeters of lead or a couple of meters of concrete between you and the source.

These principles are illustrated with the help of Professor Dee and Doctor Hay in the cartoon.

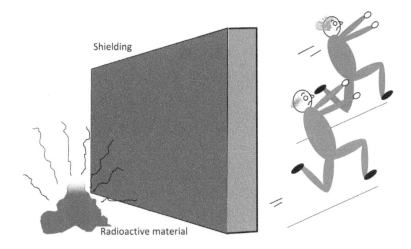

Shielding

Radioactive material

Figure 1.1 A cartoon illustration of the three basic principles of radiation protection: time, distance and shielding, with Prof Dee and Dr Hay doing a runner.

A further basic principle of radiation protection is to avoid, as much as possible, the uptake of radioactive material into the body through eating, drinking, breathing or via the contamination of a wound. Once in the body, it is usually difficult, though not impossible, to remove the radioactive contamination.

CHAPTER 2

Atoms and Radioactivity

2.1 Atoms, Elements and Radioactivity

It is known from chemistry and physics that all matter is made up of **atoms** which form the **elements** such as hydrogen, carbon, oxygen, sodium and iron. All atoms are made up of just three particles: **protons, neutrons** and **electrons**. The protons, which carry a positive electric charge, and the neutrons, which are electrically neutral, form the **atomic nucleus.** The electrons, which carry a negative electrical charge, orbit the nucleus rapidly, creating a series of "shells" around it. The atomic nucleus is some 10,000 times smaller than the diameter of the orbiting electron shells which have a diameter of about a hundred-millionth of a centimeter. Protons and neutrons have about the same mass and are around 1,800 times heavier than an electron. The number of protons and electrons in an atom is always the same so that atoms are electrically neutral. An element is identified by the number of protons in the nucleus.

As the number of protons in the nucleus increases, the number of electrons also increases to maintain electrical neutrality. As the number of electrons increases, they occupy a series of "shells" of increasing diameter with two electrons filling the innermost shell. The next two larger shells have up to eight electrons each, then two more even larger shells have up to eighteen electrons and the two largest shells have up to thirty-two electrons each. The electrons in the outer shell of a nucleus are called "**valency electrons**" and the number of valency electrons defines the chemical nature of the atom. This is why different elements have similar chemical properties. For example, lithium, sodium and potassium have similar chemical properties and each has just one electron in the outer shell, whereas helium, neon, argon, krypton and xenon each have full shells and form the series of chemically unreactive, so-called, "noble" gases.

Prof Dee and Dr Hay's Take Home Message is:

Atoms are the building blocks of all matter. Atoms have a nucleus made up of protons and neutrons which is surrounded by orbiting electrons in shells of increasing diameter. Elements are defined by the number of protons in the nucleus. The number of valency electrons in the outer shell of the atom defines its chemical nature.

The simplest atom is the **hydrogen** atom, illustrated in figure 2.1a. The hydrogen nucleus is a single proton with a single electron orbiting it so that the atom is electrically neutral. In figure 2.1, two other forms of hydrogen known as **deuterium** and **tritium** are illustrated. Deuterium has a nucleus made up of one proton and one neutron with one electron orbiting them. The tritium nucleus (fig 2.1c) has two neutrons and one proton with one electron orbiting them.

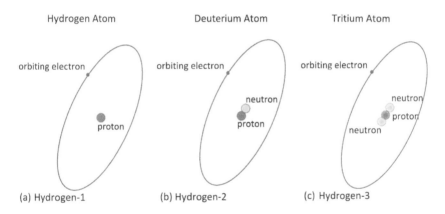

(a) Hydrogen-1   (b) Hydrogen-2   (c) Hydrogen-3

Figure 2.1 *(a) A pictorial representation of the hydrogen atom with one proton (red) in the nucleus and one orbiting electron. (b) A pictorial representation of the deuterium atom (hydrogen-2) with one proton and one neutron (green) in the nucleus and one orbiting electron. (c) A pictorial representation of the tritium atom (hydrogen-3) with one proton and two neutrons in the nucleus and one orbiting electron. (not drawn to scale)*

The single orbiting electron defines the chemical reactivity of the three forms of hydrogen where deuterium and tritium are known as **"isotopes"** or **"nuclides"** of hydrogen. Hydrogen is unusual in that the two isotopes (nuclides) have been given different names. All other isotopes (nuclides) are identified by the name of the element and the total number of protons and neutrons in the nucleus. This number is known as the **mass number** and the three forms or **nuclides** of hydrogen can be identified as hydrogen-1, hydrogen-2 (deuterium) and hydrogen-3 (tritium). This terminology is applied to all the elements, for example, oxygen-16, potassium-39, iron-59 and uranium-238.

In the tritium nucleus, the combination of two neutrons with one proton is somewhat energetically unstable so, in order to lose the excess energy, a neutron decays to a proton and the tritium nucleus emits radiation in the form of a **beta particle** which is an energetic electron. Tritium is a **radioactive isotope** of hydrogen and is also called a **radionuclide**.

Some of you might be wondering what happens to the tritium atom when it decays and the nucleus changes from one proton with two neutrons to two protons with one neutron. Well, in a process known as transmutation, it becomes a helium-3 nucleus which has two protons and one neutron.

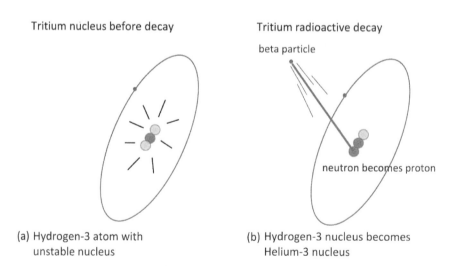

Tritium nucleus before decay

Tritium radioactive decay

beta particle

neutron becomes proton

(a) Hydrogen-3 atom with unstable nucleus

(b) Hydrogen-3 nucleus becomes Helium-3 nucleus

Figure 2.2 *A pictorial representation of the radioactive decay of tritium (hydrogen-3). (not drawn to scale)*

In general, when a nuclide (isotope) of an element has a major imbalance between the number of protons and neutrons in its nucleus, then that nuclide (isotope) is radioactive.

Dr Hay and Prof Dee's Take Home Message is:

Hydrogen is the simplest atom with one proton in its nucleus and one orbiting electron. Hydrogen has three nuclides (isotopes): hydrogen, deuterium and tritium. Tritium is radioactive. As a general rule, the excess energy resulting from the major imbalance between the number of protons and the number of neutrons in an atom's nucleus is what makes that atom radioactive.

The element which has two protons in the nucleus is **helium**. Helium-4 has two protons and two neutrons in the nucleus and two electrons in orbit around the nucleus filling the first shell. Because the first shell is "full", the helium element is particularly unreactive chemically. The helium-4 atom is illustrated in figure 2.3. Helium has two stable nuclides (isotopes): helium-4 and helium-3. Interestingly, a form of radiation that you will encounter later called an **alpha particle** is made up of two protons and two neutrons and is thus identical with the helium-4 nucleus.

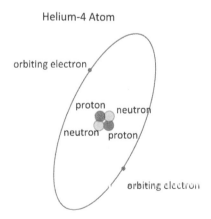

Helium-4 Atom

Figure 2.3 *A pictorial representation of the helium-4 atom. (not drawn to scale)*

The next element with three protons is lithium which has two orbiting electrons filling the inner shell and one orbiting electron in its outer second shell. Lithium is followed by berylium with 4 protons and 4 orbiting electrons and then comes boron with 5 protons and 5 orbiting electrons. After them come the interesting elements that are associated with life: carbon with 6 protons and 6 electrons, nitrogen with 7 protons and 7 electrons and oxygen with 8 protons and 8 electrons. Carbon has a radioactive isotope (radionuclide), carbon-14, with 6 protons and 8 neutrons and 6 orbiting electrons. The carbon-14 nucleus emits a beta particle and one neutron is converted to a proton so that the nucleus left after decay, nitrogen-14, has 7 neutrons and 7 protons. The stable atom of carbon-12 and the radioactive atom of carbon-14 are illustrated in figure 2.4 and the stable atoms of nitrogen-14 and oxygen-16 are illustrated in figure 2.5.

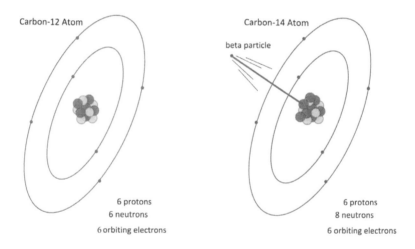

Figure 2.4 *A pictorial representation of the stable atom of carbon-12 and the radioactive atom of carbon-14. (not drawn to scale)*

All the naturally occurring elements on earth can be listed according to their increasing number of protons from hydrogen with one proton up to uranium-238 with 92 protons. As the number of protons in the nucleus of an element increases, so does the number of possible nuclides (isotopes) of that element. For example, hydrogen with one proton has three nuclides (isotopes) with zero, one and two neutrons, whereas iron

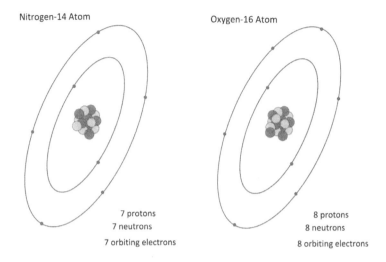

Figure 2.5 *A pictorial representation of the stable atoms of nitrogen-14 and oxygen-16. (not drawn to scale)*

with 26 protons has ten nuclides (isotopes) from iron-51 to iron-61 with the corresponding number of neutrons increasing from 25 to 35. Lighter elements with a low number of protons tend to have stable nuclides with about equal numbers of protons and neutrons but heavier elements with larger numbers of protons tend to have stable nuclides with more neutrons than protons.

And the Take Home Message is:

As the number of protons and neutrons in the nucleus increases, we move up the list of elements from the lightest, hydrogen, to the heaviest, uranium, and the number of possible nuclides (isotopes) increases. Stable nuclides of the lighter elements have equal numbers of protons and neutrons but stable nuclides of the heavier elements tend to have more neutrons than protons.

Each of the elements that are encountered in daily life is made up of a mixture of the different nuclides of that element, usually with one of the stable nuclides forming the dominant component. Although almost all of the nuclides are stable, some of the elements will have one or more radionuclides in the mix and this means that you are always surrounded by small amounts of radioactive materials.

Unstable nuclides with too many neutrons decay to a more stable state by emitting a **beta particle** (an energetic electron) and changing a neutron to a proton, just like the tritium example above. When the new nucleus still has excess energy, this is often emitted as a penetrating **gamma ray**. Unstable nuclides with too many protons convert to a more stable state by emitting a positively charged particle, a **positron**, and changing a proton into a neutron.

Some of the heavier nuclides with high mass numbers decay by emitting an energetic **alpha particle** or helium-4 nucleus. All these unstable nuclides which lose energy by emitting charged particles and gamma rays are radioactive and can be found, generally in very small amounts, in the soil, water and air around us. Large amounts of a series of radionuclides, known as fission products because they arise in the splitting, or fission, of the uranium-235 atom, are produced in nuclear reactors.

Prof Dee and Dr Hay's Take Home Message is:

Most of the nuclides are stable but one or two are radioactive so we are all surrounded by small amounts of radioactivity. Nuclides with too many neutrons decay by emitting a beta particle often with a gamma ray. Some heavy nuclides decay by emitting an alpha particle. Large amounts of radionuclides, called fission products, are produced in nuclear reactors.

2.2 Becquerels and Half-Lives

A radioactive material emits its radiation in all directions and randomly in time. The amount, or **activity**, of a radionuclide is now measured in a unit called the **becquerel** (Bq) where one becquerel equals the decay of one atomic nucleus per second, on average. Because all radioactive decay occurs spontaneously and at random, the decay process is not as regular as clockwork. The becquerel is a very small unit and activity is often expressed in units of a thousand bequerels or kilobequerels (kBq) or even a million becquerels or megabecquerels (MBq). The becquerel is named after the French scientist, Henri Becquerel, who first discovered radioactivity in uranium salts. The old unit of activity, which may be more familiar, was called the **curie** after Marie Curie who discovered the radioactive elements radium and polonium. The curie is a very much larger unit of radioactivity than the becquerel.

Each radioactive isotope or radionuclide is characterised by the type and energy of the radiation that it emits and by its unique rate of decay or **half-life**. The half-life of a radionuclide is defined as the time it takes for the amount of radioactivity to decrease by one half. This means that the radioactivity decreases from its initial value to ½ and then to ¼ and then to ⅛ etc. in successive half-lives with the result that, from a knowledge of the initial activity and the half-life, the amount of radioactivity can be accurately predicted for any time in the future. All radionuclides decay in this way.

An example of radioactive decay is shown in figure 2.6 which plots "Activity" against "Number of half-lives" for a radioactive isotope (radionuclide) with an initial activity of 1,000 becquerels. This type of decay is known as **exponential** decay. It never gets to zero although it does eventually become very small and the figure shows that, after 10 half-lives, the amount of radioactivity is reduced by a factor of about 1,000.

And Our Take Home Message is:

A radioactive isotope (radionuclide) is characterised by the type and energy of the radiation it emits and by its unique half-life. Activity is measured in becquerels. All radioactivity exhibits exponential decay over time.

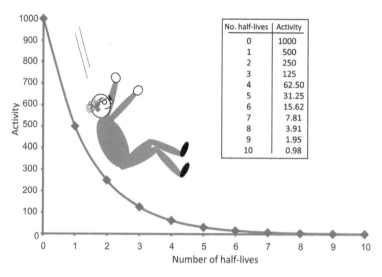

Figure 2.6 *A graphical representation of the decay of radioactivity with time. Activity (A), starting at 1,000 becquerels, is plotted on the Y-axis (vertical) against the number of half-lives (N), starting at zero, which is plotted on the X-axis (horizontal). The blue diamonds represent the activity after an increasing number of half-lives, as shown in the data box in the graph. The red line illustrates the shape of the exponential decay of radioactivity.*

The curve shown in the figure can be transformed to become a straight line by changing the scale of the "Activity" axis (vertical) from a normal scale to a **logarithmic** scale. This is shown in figure 2.7. Logarithms are like code-breakers for exponential functions. The logarithmic scale is broken down into decades (1000 to 100 to 10 to 1 etc.), and the subdivision within each of the decades is bunched towards the higher end, but the scale never becomes zero. The straight line is more convenient for estimating radioactivity accurately at a later time.

For the more mathematical amongst you, the curve in figure 2.6 and the straight line in figure 2.7 are described by the equation:

$$A_N = A_0 \exp(-0.693N),$$

where N is the number of half-lives, A_0 the initial activity when N = 0, A_N is the activity at half-life N and 'exp' is an abbreviation for an exponential function.

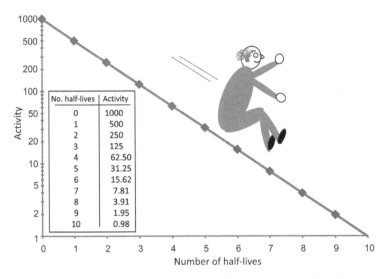

No. half-lives	Activity
0	1000
1	500
2	250
3	125
4	62.50
5	31.25
6	15.62
7	7.81
8	3.91
9	1.95
10	0.98

Figure 2.7 *The same data as used in figure 2.6 are plotted using a 'logarithmic scale' for the level of activity on the Y-axis. The use of the 'logarithmic scale' converts the descending curve, seen in figure 2.6, into a straight line.*

[Throughout the book the graphical curves will be colour-coded with the appropriate mathematical equations for clarity. It is not necessary to understand the mathematics of the equations but it is helpful to appreciate their significance. So, in figures 2.6 and 2.7 the red lines demonstrate the significance of the red equation, namely the decrease in radioactivity with time, emphasized by Dr Hay and Prof Dee.]

The red equation can be rewritten so that it can be applied to radionuclides which have different half-lives by realising that the number of half-lives (N) is equal to the time elapsed (T) divided by the value of the half-life (λ), that is $N = T/λ$. The red equation thus becomes:

$$A_T = A_0 \exp(-0.693T/λ),$$

where λ is the half-life, T the time elapsed, A_0 the initial activity at time T = 0, A_T is the activity at time T, and 'exp' is an abbreviation for an exponential function. This equation can be used to calculate the remaining activity of any radionuclide at any future time if the half-life of that radionuclide and its activity at time zero are known.

17

The half-lives of different radionuclides are accurately known and vary from a fraction of a second to billions of years.

Radionuclide	Half-life	Famous for
Radon-222	3.82 days	seeping into houses built on granite
Iodine-131	8 days	volatile fission product in reactors
Caesium-137	30 years	volatile fission product in reactors
Radium-226	1600 years	first purified by Marie Curie
Tritium (hydrogen-3)	12.3 years	used in radioluminescent indicators
Uranium-238	4470 million years	natural radioactivity

Figure 2.6 can be used to compare the environmental impact of two radionuclides, iodine-131 and caesium-137, which, being volatile elements, were released as gases in the Chernobyl reactor fire and contaminated parts of northern Europe. Iodine-131 with a half-life of 8 days was only important in the immediate aftermath of the fire and had decayed by a factor 1,000 in 80 days even though it caused many thyroid cancers in young children exposed in the surroundings of Chernobyl. Caesium-137, on the other hand, with a half-life of 30 years will be with us in the areas which were contaminated for many, many years to come, even though it has not caused any detectable health effects so far.

And the Take Home Message is:

Radioactive decay can be described by a mathematical equation so that by knowing the activity and half-life of a radionuclide, its activity at any time in the future can be calculated accurately.

And, by the way, it is useful to know that "exp(0) = 1", "exp(-n) decreases from 1 as n gets bigger but never reaches 0", and "exp(n) increases from 1 ever more quickly as n gets bigger".

2.3 Natural and Man-Made Radioactivity

All the elements and their radioactive isotopes (radionuclides) were created many billions of years ago during star formation in the early history of the Universe. Consequently, all the radioactive isotopes with half-lives of less than a few billion years have long since decayed to stable nuclides but there are some that remain and form the source of most of the natural radioactivity which surrounds us. Indeed, three heavy radionuclides, uranium-238, thorium-232, and to a lesser extent uranium-235, with half-lives of billions of years, each initiate a whole chain of radioactive nuclide decays with the emission of alpha particles and beta particles. These form the basis of much of our natural radioactivity. One example is shown in figure 2.8 which presents the chain of decays arising from uranium-238, with a half-life of 4.5 billion years, down to the stable nuclide of lead-206. The figure carries a lot of information and is worth studying carefully as an understanding of it will facilitate an appreciation of the different radioactive decay processes.

The figure shows the decay series starting with uranium-238 and including radium-226 (associated with Marie Curie) and radon-222, a gas which can seep into houses built on top of granite deposits. Uranium-238 decays by alpha particle emission to become thorium-234, which then decays by beta/gamma emission to become protactinium-234, which also decays by beta/gamma emission to become uranium-234. Uranium-234 starts a series of alpha particle decays which takes it through thorium-230, radium-226, radon-222, polonium-218 to lead-214. The series of radioactive decays finally ends with the stable nuclide of lead-206.

Another natural radionuclide with a long half-life of 1,250 million years is potassium-40 which is still found in the environment and also in man. A small fraction of the potassium in your bodies is radioactive though the levels are not dangerous.

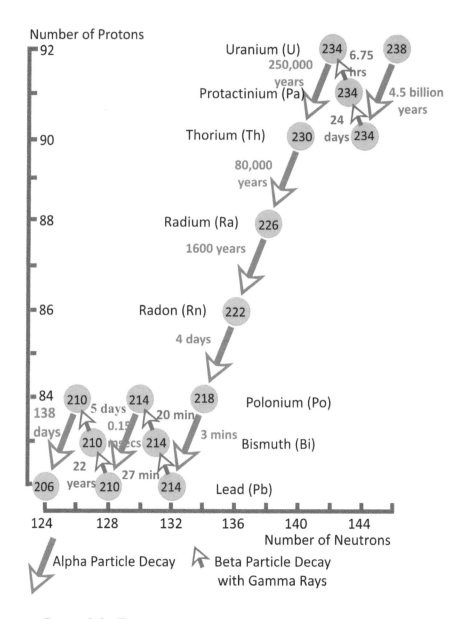

Figure 2.8 *The radioactive decay of uranium-238 and its daughter radionuclides to the stable nuclide lead-206. The numbers in the blue discs are mass numbers (no. protons + no. neutrons). Alpha particle decay takes two protons and two neutrons out of the nucleus. Beta particle decay converts one neutron into a proton. The half-life of each decay in years, days, hours, minutes and seconds is presented and the names of the elements are given together with their abbreviations opposite the appropriate proton number.*

Carbon-14 is also a naturally occurring radionuclide but with a difference because its half-life is only 5,730 years. Carbon-14 is being continually formed in the upper atmosphere by the action of cosmic radiation on nitrogen-14. It is deposited on earth and can be used in archeological dating (carbon dating).

Tritium-3, on the other hand, is a by-product of the nuclear industry as are a large number of other radionuclides with relatively short half-lives. They are created using nuclear reactors or accelerators for specific use, for example, in diagnostic and therapeutic medicine. Other man-made radionuclides arise as fission products or as transuranic (heavier than uranium) radionuclides, such as plutonium-239, in nuclear power reactors. Some of the transuranic radionuclides have long half-lives and create the problem of disposal of high-level radioactive waste from the nuclear industry.

All radioactive decay occurs spontaneously and at random and it can therefore be neither turned on nor, more importantly, turned off.

Dr Hay and Prof Dee's Take Home Message is:

We are all surrounded by small amounts of natural radioactivity created in the early history of the universe. Only radionuclides with ultra long half-lives (billions of years) and their radioactive decay products remain and most elements are stable. And, remember, radioactivity cannot be turned on and it cannot be turned off.

CHAPTER 3

Radiation

3.1 The Different Radiations

Six different types of radiation are identified here. They are the most common ones that you might encounter or be exposed to. These are alpha particles, beta particles, gamma rays, X-rays, neutrons and protons. These radiations have different penetrations and different biological damage-inducing efficiencies. There are other more exotic types of radiation but they are usually produced by special particle accelerators.

Alpha particle (α) – made up of two protons and two neutrons and emitted with considerable energies in a straight line **track** by heavier radionuclides. An alpha particle carries a double positive electrical charge from the two protons and therefore loses energy by interacting vigorously with the electrons in the shells of the atoms of normal matter that it passes through. It can, therefore, be stopped by a sheet of paper or the superficial, dead layer of skin. Alpha particles are particularly damaging biologically but, because of their low penetration of tissue, they only form a radiation hazard if the alpha emitter is taken up into the body by eating, drinking or breathing or via the contamination of a wound. Once incorporated into the body, the alpha particles can cause considerable biological damage. The Russian dissident, Alexander Litvinenko, was almost certainly "poisoned" in London in 2006 by unwittingly consuming a small amount of alpha particle emitting polonium.

Beta particle (β) – an electron (negative electrical charge) emitted with considerable energies by a wide variety of radionuclides and often accompanied by gamma ray emission. Beta particles lose energy by interacting with the electrons of the atoms of normal matter and are scattered in a tortuous track. They can penetrate a centimeter or so of water, plastic or tissue and can therefore damage superficial organs, such

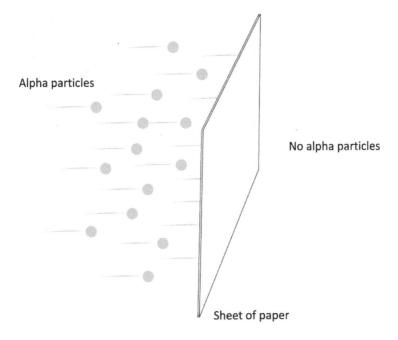

Figure 3.1 *A pictorial representation of alpha particles being stopped completely by a sheet of paper. (not drawn to scale)*

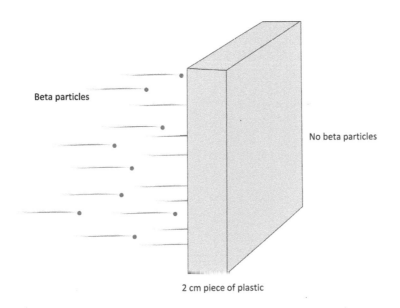

Figure 3.2 *A pictorial representation of beta particles being completely stopped by a two centimeter piece of plastic. (not drawn to scale)*

as the eyes, but they are not a radiation hazard for internal organs of the body unless the beta emitter is taken up in the body by eating, drinking or breathing or by the contamination of a wound. Beta particles are much less biologically damaging than alpha particles.

Gamma radiation (γ) – falls into the same type of radiation as visible light, microwaves and radio waves but has a much shorter wavelength and is therefore much more energetic.

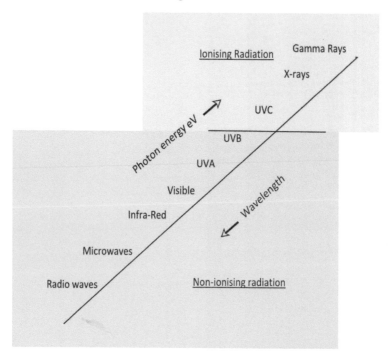

Figure 3.3 *The complete spectrum of electromagnetic radiation from the very short wavelength, energetic gamma rays to the very long wavelength, low energy radio waves.*

This type of radiation is classified as "**electro-magnetic**" radiation with the spectrum running from the high energy, short wavelength, gamma rays through the ultraviolet (UV), visible and infra-red regions to the lower energy, long wavelength, microwaves and radio waves (see figure 3.3). Gamma rays are often referred to as "photons" in much the same way as light photons, although the gamma ray photon energy is much larger than the light photon energy. Gamma rays are very penetrating, losing their energy very gradually in scattering interactions with the electrons of the atoms making up normal matter. They are safely attenuated, although not completely stopped, by several centimeters of lead or a few meters of concrete. Although gamma rays are much less biologically damaging than alpha particles, they easily penetrate the body and are therefore an important external radiation hazard.

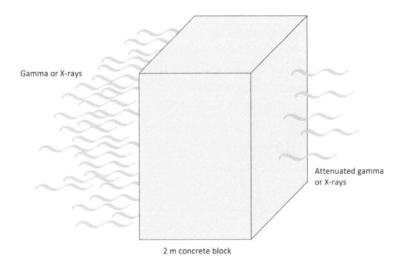

Gamma or X-rays

Attenuated gamma or X-rays

2 m concrete block

Figure 3.4 *A pictorial representation of gamma or X-rays being attenuated but not completely stopped by two meters of concrete. The intensity of the gamma or X-rays is considerably reduced by the concrete. (not drawn to scale)*

X-rays – are also electro-magnetic radiation, like gamma rays, but are given a different name because they are produced by a machine, whereas gamma rays are emitted by radioactive isotopes. They are usually somewhat less energetic than gamma rays but they easily penetrate the body and are therefore also an external radiation hazard. X-rays, because they are lower in energy than gamma rays, are safely attenuated by a few centimeters of lead or a meter or so of concrete. Importantly, the X-ray machine can always be turned off. It is worth noting here that the amount of radiation normally used in X-ray radiography examinations for broken bones, for example, is very small.

Neutrons (n) – are electrically neutral and are produced in large numbers in nuclear reactors but can also be produced in special reactions by particle accelerators. Energetic neutrons (**fast neutrons**) lose their energy in 'billiard ball' type collisions with the nuclei of atoms in the matter they pass through. However, they lose little energy bouncing off the heavier atoms (think of a tennis ball bouncing off a football), but a much larger amount of energy bouncing off the proton nucleus of hydrogen atoms. The transfer of a substantial amount of energy from the fast neutron to the proton creates an "energetic" **proton**. As they pass through water or human tissue rich in hydrogen and slow down, the fast neutrons create a shower of energetic protons. Fast neutrons penetrate the body easily and are therefore an external radiation hazard because they create secondary proton radiation inside the body. The energetic **recoil protons,** with their positive electrical charge, interact quite vigorously with the electrons of the atoms of normal matter and are more biologically damaging than gamma rays, X-rays and beta particles but are not very penetrating. Fast neutrons are most easily slowed down in a few meters of hydrogenous material such as water and the 'slow' or '**thermal' neutrons** finally produced are readily absorbed by the two elements, boron and cadmium.

Prof Dee and Dr Hay's Take Home Message is:

There are six different types of radiation of most concern to us. Three of them, alpha particles, beta particles and gamma rays, are associated with radioactivity. Alpha particles and protons are very effective biologically but not very penetrating. Gamma rays are similar to X-rays and are very penetrating but less effective biologically. Beta particles are not as penetrating as gamma rays but have a similar biological effectiveness. Fast neutrons, on the other hand, are penetrating, create energetic recoil protons (hydrogen nuclei) and are thus biologically effective.

3.2 Radiation Interaction with Matter

All these radiations, except for neutrons, interact with the electrons of the atoms of normal matter as they pass through it. The interactions between the radiations and the electrons invariably transfer sufficient energy to the electrons to knock them out of their shells and send them on their way as energetic secondary electrons, rather like secondary beta particles. The atom that has lost an ejected electron carries a positive electrical charge and is called an **ion**. With each interaction, the radiation loses some energy and "slows down" a bit. The radiation passing through matter thus creates a shower of energetic secondary electrons which, in turn, create cascades of lower energy electrons that have quite closely packed ionising interactions at their **track-ends**. This goes on until the radiation and its secondary electrons no longer have sufficient energy to knock the atomic electrons out of the shells. At this point, the radiation has lost all its initial energy and come to rest. The ejection of the electrons from the shells of the atoms is called "**ionisation**" and the six types of radiation (alpha particles, beta particles, gamma rays, X-rays, neutrons and protons) are called "**ionising radiations**".

Because a positive electrical charge attracts a negative electrical charge and repels a positive electrical charge, alpha particles with a double positive charge, protons with one positive charge and beta particles with one negative charge interact directly with the negatively charged electrons of the atoms and are known as "**directly ionising radiations**".

Gamma rays and X-rays which interact indirectly with the electrons of the atoms through scattering, and fast neutrons which have first to collide with a hydrogen nucleus and create an energetic recoil proton, are called "**indirectly ionising radiations**".

You will see later that the ionisation process is capable of breaking molecular bonds formed by the valency electrons of different elements and compounds to create chemically active species which are called "**free radicals**".

 Dr Hay and Prof Dee's Take Home Message is:

Essentially, all ionising radiation interacts with matter by knocking electrons out of atomic shells and thus breaking chemical bonds.

3.3 Detection and Measurement of Radiation

Detection Methods – None of the human senses permit us to detect any of these radiations even though we can see visible light which is the same type of radiation as gamma rays and X-rays, though of much lower energy. However, there are several ways by which the radiations can be detected.

The ionisation process, when it occurs in a gas, produces free, positively charged ions and negatively charged electrons so, if there is a way of collecting these charges with, for example, two metal plates connected one to each pole of a battery, we can measure a current induced in the gas by the radiation. The more radiation, the bigger the current. This is a basic description of an **ionisation chamber** and works well when there is sufficient radiation.

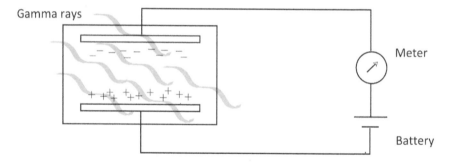

Figure 3.5 *A simple diagram of how an ionisation chamber can be used to measure a current of electricity caused by the gamma ray-induced positive and negative charges in air.*

A **geiger-muller counter** is used to detect and measure small amounts of radioactivity. It is similar to an ionisation chamber except that it is designed to accelerate the negative electrical charges produced by a radiation track in the gas towards a high voltage wire. This creates an avalanche of electrical charge at the wire and a pulse of electricity which can be counted electronically and made to make a 'click' sound on a speaker. The more clicks, the more radioactivity.

Old fashioned photographic film is darkened by exposure to radiation and the degree of darkening can be used to measure radiation exposure. In the past, radiation workers used to wear a photographic "film badge" to measure and document their exposure. Henri Bequerel originally discovered radioactivity in 1896 because the radiation from some uranium salts he was studying caused the darkening of his light-sealed photographic plates. When the photographic plates were developed, he could see images of coins placed between them and the uranium salts.

There are other, more modern methods of detecting radiation such as **thermo-luminescence**. Crystals of lithium fluoride, for example, store the energy absorbed from a radiation exposure in the crystal lattice and release it as light when the crystals are heated above a critical temperature. The amount of light emitted is a measure of the radiation exposure to the crystals.

It should be clear that, because alpha particles are absorbed by a single piece of paper, it is very difficult to detect alpha particle radioactivity and therefore special techniques are needed. One such technique is **liquid scintillation counting**. Paper tissue wipes of a material suspected of being contaminated with alpha radioactivity are dissolved in a liquid that reacts to an alpha particle passing through it by giving a light pulse which can be counted. Fortunately, much alpha activity is accompanied by other, more easily detected, radiations. The great difficulty of finding pure alpha activity is the reason it was so hard to identify what Litvinenko had been poisoned with. However, the traces of alpha radioactivity in London made it possible to locate exactly where the poison had been.

And Our Take Home Message is:

Although we humans cannot detect ionising radiation, there are many different methods, using chemistry and physics, of not only detecting radiation but also of accurately measuring it.

3.4 Energy of Radiation

The energy of ionising radiations is measured in units of **"electron volts"** (eV). One electron volt is the energy given by accelerating a single electric charge across a voltage of one volt. Actually, multiples of the electron volt are invariably used such as kilo-electron volts (keV), or a thousand electron volts, and Mega-electron volts (MeV), or a million electron volts. Alpha particles are usually emitted with energies of around 5MeV. Beta particles vary between 1MeV (maximum) from iodine-131 to 15keV (maximum) from tritium. Gamma rays are usually in the range of 600keV for caesium-137 to 1MeV for cobalt-60. The energy of X-rays depends on the voltage of the machine used to produce them but, in diagnostic medicine, 90keV X-rays are used for mammography and energies from 150keV to 250keV are used to investigate bone fractures. In medical radiotherapy treatments, higher energies of X-rays are produced by accelerators. Interestingly, especially because it is counter-intuitive, the lower energy X-rays are somewhat more biologically effective than the higher energy X-rays and gamma rays. Fast neutrons created by a nuclear reactor have energies around 1MeV but 14MeV neutrons can be produced by accelerators and have been used in medical radiotherapy treatments.

3.5 Dose and Dose Rate

The amount of energy that radiation deposits in matter is called **"absorbed dose"** and is measured in units given the name **"gray"** (Gy) after the English radiation physicist, L Harold Gray. One gray is equal to the absorption of one joule of energy in one kilogram of material. You should remember that one gray of alpha particle radiation is much more biologically effective than one gray of beta particle radiation or gamma and X-radiation. Although 4 to 5 joules of energy in a kilogram of water is not going to raise the temperature of the water very much, it is useful to realise that 4 to 5 gray (Gy) of gamma or X-radiation absorbed in the total human body will kill a person within a couple of weeks. Clearly, the way in which the energy is deposited in the body is crucial for the radiation effect.

It is important to realise that radioactivity measured in becquerels means that a certain number of disintegrations occur per second, on average. Time is, therefore, an important parameter in radiation exposure. If you are exposed to two hundred becquerels for one hour, you will accumulate one half of the dose you would get if you were exposed for two hours and thus it is relevant to talk about the "**dose-rate**" emitted by a source of radioactivity. The same applies to radiation from an X-ray machine where the beam current can be adjusted to give a desired "dose rate". Dose rate is measured in gray per hour (Gy/hr) and it will be seen later that, while 4 to 5 Gy of gamma or X-radiation accumulated in a few minutes will kill, spreading the same exposure or dose over several days, will not kill.

Prof Dee and Dr Hay's Take Home Message is:

The amount or dose of radiation is measured in "grays" but 1 gray of alpha particles is more biologically damaging than 1 gray of gamma rays. A total body dose of 4 to 5 grays of gamma rays in a short time will kill. Radioactivity is measured in "disintegrations per second" and we talk about the dose-rate emitted by a radioactive source.

3.6   Background Radiation

The presence of natural radioactivity means that some of the elements we encounter in everyday life have isotopes which are radioactive and that radioactivity, although very small in amount, is present in the air, water and soil around us. So, everyone is exposed to some very small amounts of radiation and no one can escape it. This radiation is called "**natural background radiation**" because it is not man-made. Another component of natural background radiation comes from outer space and is called "**cosmic radiation**". Those living at high altitudes have a slightly bigger "**background dose**" than those who live by the sea. People who live in houses built on granite rock deposits, such as are found in Cornwall or Aberdeen in the UK, also have a higher background dose which comes from radon gas seeping into the house from the granite. Granite has small amounts of uranium-238 in it and, in figure 2.8 which shows the decay scheme of this radionuclide, you can find radium-226 that decays to the gas radon-222. Radon gas can seep out of the granite through cracks and concentrate in the basements of houses where it decays further to polonium-218 and other short-lived alpha and beta particle-emitting radionuclides. These radionuclides attach to dust particles and can be inhaled to irradiate lung tissue. Another example of background radiation comes from potassium which is much more common than uranium and is taken up in the body in food. About 100 parts per million of potassium is potassium-40 which is radioactive and emits gamma rays. This means that everyone is slightly radioactive and thus you are all constantly exposing yourselves and anyone else who gets close to you to very small amounts of radiation!

All these components of natural background radiation can be added together to give the "natural background radiation dose" but only when the biological effectiveness of the different radiations is taken into account. To facilitate this, the "**International Commission on Radiological Protection**" (ICRP), an independent body set up to protect and regulate the general population and those who work with radiation, has defined a special unit of "**equivalent dose**" called the "**sievert**" (Sv), named after the Swedish radiation physicist, Rolf Sievert. The ICRP has decided that one gray of gamma rays and beta particles is equivalent to one sievert but one gray of alpha particles is equivalent to twenty sievert. For most of the population, the yearly natural background radiation dose from all the different sources is estimated to be about two and a half thousandths of a sievert (2.5 millisieverts). It is, therefore, not considered to be a significant health risk.

Dr Hay and Prof Dee's Take Home Message is:

We are all exposed to natural radiation in the air, water and soil around us and from radiation coming from outer space. The ICRP have defined an "equivalent dose" measured in "sievert" to take account of the biological effectiveness of different radiations so that they can add all the components of background radiation together.

The ICRP estimates that our annual natural background radiation dose amounts to two and a half thousandths of a sievert (2.5 millisieverts) which is not a health risk.

And let's not forget that, while we need to be careful of our exposure to radiation, it does have many beneficial uses!

CHAPTER 4

Molecules, the Cell, Chromosomes and DNA

4.1 Molecules

Atoms, which make up the elements that form the building blocks of all matter, can combine to form larger units called **molecules**. Atoms may combine with themselves or with atoms of different elements. A hydrogen atom can combine with itself to form a hydrogen molecule, denoted H_2, or two atoms of hydrogen can combine with one atom of oxygen to form a water molecule, denoted H_2O. One atom of sodium (Na) can combine with one atom of chlorine (Cl) to form sodium chloride or common salt, denoted NaCl. In all the combinations of different atoms to form molecules, it is the electrons in the outer shells of the atoms, the 'valency electrons', which are shared and hold the molecule together. These shared electrons form the chemical bond. This is illustrated for the hydrogen molecule and the water molecule in figure 4.1. Combining atoms is, essentially, what chemistry is all about.

One branch of chemistry, organic chemistry, deals, more or less, with combinations of hydrogen, carbon, nitrogen and oxygen and these four elements are what humans are mainly made up of. The human body consists of water, calcium and large and complicated molecules of proteins, enzymes, sugars etc. formed from the four elements.

Ionising radiation interacts with the electrons in the atoms which make up these molecules and invariably ejects electrons from them. Although radiation does not always react with the valency electrons but also with other inner shell electrons, the result of the ejection of an electron is that the chemical bonds holding the molecules together are broken. When radiation interacts with a water molecule and ejects an electron, the resulting electrically charged water molecule breaks up to create a **hydroxyl radical** (OH) made up of an oxygen atom and a hydrogen

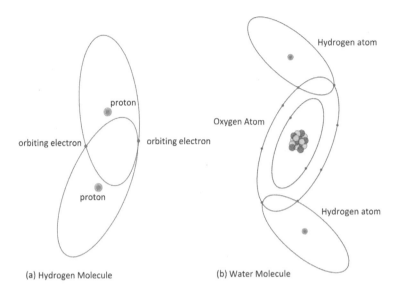

Figure 4.1 *(a) A pictorial representation of a hydrogen molecule with two hydrogen atoms sharing their two electrons. (b) A pictorial representation of a water molecule with two atoms of hydrogen and one atom of oxygen. The hydrogen atoms share their electrons with electrons in the outer shell of the oxygen atom. (not drawn to scale)*

atom. These **hydroxyl free radicals** are a very reactive chemical species and can attack and damage other important molecules in their close neighbourhood. Therefore, it is not just the direct action of radiation breaking chemical bonds, but also the indirect and damaging effect of the free radical species on other molecules, which is responsible for the radiation effect.

And Our Take Home Message is:

Atoms combine to form molecules by sharing electrons in their outer shells. The shared electrons are called valency electrons and form the chemical bonds which hold the molecules together. All ionising radiations eject electrons, though not necessarily the valency electrons, from atoms and molecules and break chemical bonds. When a water molecule is broken by radiation, a reactive free radical is created which can also attack other molecules.

4.2 The Cell and its Nucleus

Nearly all the cells in the human body are made up of an outer wall which contains the cytoplasm which in turn surrounds a nucleus held within a nuclear envelope or membrane. The cell nucleus should not be confused with the atomic nucleus discussed earlier. The cell nucleus contains the **chromosomes** which each have a backbone of **DNA**. The chromosomes, via all their DNA, carry all the genetic information which determines the operation and nature of the cell.

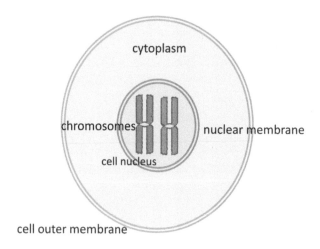

Figure 4.2 *A pictorial representation of a cell showing the essential components including chromosomes in the cell nucleus. (not drawn to scale) The diameter of a cell is a few thousandths of a millimeter and one gram of tissue contains a billion cells.*

In the body, there is an ongoing, slow turnover of cells. As the cells die, they are replaced by similar new cells. Most of the cells in an adult are either not dividing or only slowly dividing but in some tissues, such as the blood or the lining of the stomach, they are constantly dividing. The dividing cell cycle has been broken down into four parts: a first gap (G_1), a **DNA synthesis** phase (S), a second gap (G_2) and cell division or **mitosis** (M). G_1 seems to be a period when the cell prepares for DNA synthesis. The S phase is the period when the DNA in the chromosomes is replicated and the nucleus acquires a double set of chromosomes. G_2 seems to be a period when the cell prepares to divide into two new cells.

And mitosis (M) is the phase when the two sets of chromosomes are separated and the cell divides to create two new daughter cells that are exact copies of the original.

A population of cells which divide by mitosis grows rapidly; 1 cell gives 2 then 4 then 8 then 16 etc. (see figure 4.3) in what is known as "exponential growth". Normal healthy cells do not divide indefinitely but become stationary when further division is not needed, for example, when an organ is fully grown. These are so-called 'differentiated' cells which are unable to return to the division process. Cancer cells, on the other hand, do not respect the signal to stop dividing and the figure illustrates the dangerous 'run-away' growth of these cells.

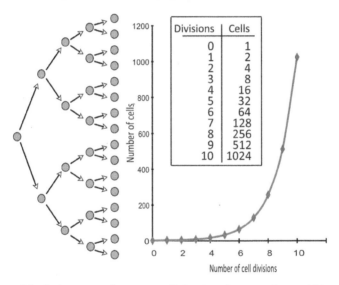

Divisions	Cells
0	1
1	2
2	4
3	8
4	16
5	32
6	64
7	128
8	256
9	512
10	1024

Figure 4.3 *A diagram of mitotic cell division showing the rapid increase in the number of cells with each ongoing division. The right side shows a graphical representation of this form of exponential growth. The blue diamonds plot the data in the data box.*

There are also cells in the body which retain the ability to divide when needed, for example, to restore tissue damage following trauma. These cells are called "**stem**" cells and each organ of the body has a pool of these cells. When these cells are called upon to divide, they undergo the mitotic cycle described above but only one of the two new daughter cells goes on to divide again and again. The other stops dividing and returns to the stem cell pool. In this way, the organs of the body are maintained over the lifetime.

In addition to the normal tissue cells in the body which are called "**somatic**" cells, there are the egg cells (oocytes) in the female and the sperm-producing cells (spermatocytes) in the male which are called "**germ**" cells and are involved in sexual reproduction.

And the Take Home Message is:

Cells have an outer membrane, a cytoplasm and a nucleus which contains the chromosomes. The dividing cell cycle has four parts: G_1, S (DNA synthesis), G_2 and M (mitosis or cell division). Normal cells do not divide indefinitely but each organ has a pool of stem cells to replace dying cells. Cancer cells do divide indefinitely. In addition to the normal somatic cells we also have germ cells for sexual reproduction.

4.3   The Human Chromosomes and DNA

In each human cell nucleus there are 46 chromosomes that constitute the **genome** of each cell, 23 from the mother and 23 from the father. There are two chromosomes which determine gender, the X chromosome and the Y chromosome. Females have two X chromosomes, one from their mother and one from their father, males have one X from their mother and a Y from their father. The other 44 chromosomes are made up of 22 **homologous** pairs, one each from their mother and their father. The two chromosomes, which form a homologous pair, are not completely identical but very similar and they carry the same genes which might, for example, determine eye colour. The homologous pairs of chromosomes are numbered by convention from one, the longest, to twenty-two, the shortest. The chromosomes, a word meaning coloured bodies, can only be seen in the normal microscope when the cells are in mitosis and when the chromosomes are fully contracted or condensed. When the cells are in the other phases of the cell cycle, the chromosomes are unravelled and cannot be seen in the microscope.

The backbone of a chromosome is the **DNA double helix** which runs continuously from one end of the chromosome to the other. The 2 meters of DNA per cell is consequently divided between the 46 chromosomes. The ends of the chromosomes are called **telomeres** and, about half-way between the telomeres, the chromosomes have a **centromere**. In the G_1 phase of the cell cycle, the chromosomes have a single DNA backbone and can be represented with two arms on either side of the centromere but, after DNA synthesis, in the G_2 phase and in mitosis, the chromosomes are in a duplicated form and have four arms (see figure 4.4).

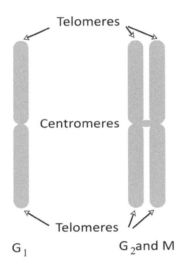

Telomeres

Centromeres

Telomeres

G_1 G_2 and M

Figure 4.4 *A pictorial representation of a G_1 chromosome with two arms and a centromere and of a G_2 and mitosis (M) chromosome with four arms and a centromere.*

It is the duplicated form of the chromosomes that is seen in the microscope. The centromere has an important function in separating the replicated chromosomes into two groups as mitosis approaches. Each group contains all 46 chromosomes, ready to go into the nucleus of the two new cells formed at mitosis.

And Our Take Home Message is:

Each of our cells has **46** chromosomes, **23** from Mum and **23** from Dad. **2** chromosomes (X and Y) determine sex and the other **44** form **22** pairs of homologous (very similar) chromosomes. Each chromosome has a DNA backbone. The ends of the chromosomes are called telomeres and each chromosome has a centromere which is used to separate the replicated chromosomes when the cell divides.

The DNA double helix molecule carries the genetic code which controls the functioning of the cells and determines the many different attributes which create each individual human being.

The double helix structure of the DNA molecule was defined by Watson and Crick in 1953 using X-ray crystallography photographs of the molecule made by Wilkins, Franklin and Gosling. The molecule has two separate, long polymer chains wound round each other in a double helix. The two polymer chains are formed from alternating sugar units and phosphate units to make parallel **sugar-phosphate strands**. The two strands are held about two nanometers (2nm) apart, that is two millionths of a millimeter, by pairs of compounds called **nucleotide bases** attached to the sugar units of each strand.

There are ten base-pair junctions about every three millionths of a millimeter or three nanometers (3nm) along the strands. There are four nucleotide bases, adenine (A), cytosine (C), guanine (G) and thymine (T). Watson and Crick defined the **complementary base pairing rule** which states that adenine always pairs with thymine (A-T), and cytosine always pairs with guanine (C-G). The molecular dimensions of the bases are such that the A-T pair has exactly the same size as the C-G pair. Each complete unit of base plus sugar plus phosphate is called a nucleotide and the DNA is sometimes known as a polynucleotide chain. The DNA molecule can be imagined as a very long rope ladder, but a slightly coiled, twisted rope ladder, as the DNA is wound into a double helix (see figure 4.5).

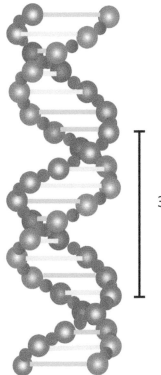

3.4 nm

Figure 4.5 A pictorial representation of a DNA double helix molecule. The two sugar-phosphate strands have been coloured blue and red to facilitate their distinction. The turquoise bars joining the two strands represent A-T or T-A base pairing and the yellow bars represent C-G or G-C base pairing. (not drawn to scale)

Watson and Crick also proposed that, because there is complementary base pairing along the DNA molecule, the sequence of the nucleotide bases formed the code which defined the genetic information. In other words, a stream of nucleotide bases along the DNA could form a **gene** that gives the code for the production of a protein. It is now known that, although this is fundamentally correct, things are a little more complicated. Although a stretch of DNA will define a gene, there are bits of that stretch of DNA that code for a part of the protein, called "**exons**", and other bits interspersed along the stretch that do not code for the protein, called "**introns**". We also know that there are stretches of DNA that have very similar sequences and are closely homologous. This DNA is called "**repetitive DNA**" and there is a substantial amount of it scattered throughout the chromosomes but its precise function is not known. About 50% of the DNA in the genome of the cell is made up of unique sequences which are probably the genes. Any disturbance of a stretch of DNA which codes for a gene will alter the protein produced and cause a **mutation** of that gene.

Prof Dee and Dr Hay's Take Home Message is:

DNA is a long thread-like molecule which carries all the genetic information. It has a double helix structure rather like a twisted, coiled rope-ladder. Two sugar-phosphate strands are held together by complementary pairs of nucleotide bases (A with T and C with G). The sequence of the nucleotides along the DNA defines the genetic code. About 50% of the DNA has unique sequences which are probably genes but there are also stretches of very similar sequences called repetitive DNA. Any change in a unique sequence of DNA will cause a mutation.

By the way, don't confuse nucleotides with the nuclides we discussed in chapter 2!

4.4 DNA Replication and Chromosome Duplication

In the DNA synthesis (S) phase of the cell cycle the chromosomes are duplicated. Knowing that the DNA molecule forms the backbone of the chromosome, and keeping the complementary base pairing rule in mind, the duplication of chromosomes can be readily understood in terms of the duplication of DNA molecules. This is because the DNA molecule is endowed with the very important ability to make a precise copy of itself. This process is called **DNA replication** during which, the two "old" strands of the DNA zip open at many points along the chromosomes. By moving in both directions along the DNA, special enzymes copy the nucleotide code of the "old" strands onto new strands at '**replication forks**'. The two "new" strands are made with exact complementary base pairing along the two "old" strands in a series of '**replicons**'. The replication forks move along the DNA until, at the 'terminus of replication' they meet another replication fork coming in the opposite direction. In this way, two new DNA double helix molecules are created that are exact copies of the old DNA helix (see figure 4.6).

Each new DNA double helix molecule has one "old" strand and one "new" strand. In this way, the chromosomes are duplicated as exact copies and what is seen in the microscope at mitosis are chromosomes each having four arms, called **chromatid arms**, with a join in the middle, called the **centromere** (see figure 4.4). The centromere holds the two identical chromosomes together until, at the end of mitosis, they separate into two new cells.

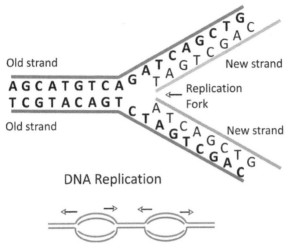

Figure 4.6 *A drawing of DNA replication. The replication fork is moving left, opening the old DNA strands and copying the DNA code of nucleotide bases onto new strands (pale colours). Underneath is a representation of two DNA replicons approaching each other. The black arrows indicate the direction of replication.*

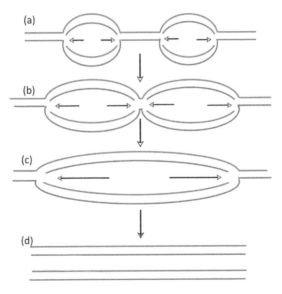

Figure 4.7 *The replication process in four stages.*

Figure 4.7 presents the process of replication in a series of drawings starting with (a) the replicons moving towards each other; (b) the replicons extending to meet; (c) the resolution of the meeting replicons and (d) the complete replication of a new stretch of DNA. Remember that each new DNA double helix has one old strand from the original double helix which is copied perfectly.

At the start of replication, a multitude of replicons is initiated along the DNA double helix in the chromosomes. The process continues until the full DNA double helix chromosome backbone is replicated.

It will be seen later that the complementary base pairing rule and the enzymes which organise DNA replication are important for the repair of radiation damage to DNA. It will also be seen that the presence of large amounts of repetitive DNA in the cell influences the repair of radiation damage.

 And Our Take Home Message is:

DNA has the remarkable ability to copy (replicate) itself perfectly during the DNA synthesis phase with the help of special enzymes in the cell nucleus. This duplicates the chromosomes held together by the centromere until, at mitosis, they separate into two new cells. Both the special replication enzymes and the repetitive DNA are important for the repair of radiation damage to DNA.

CHAPTER 5

The Effects of Radiation on DNA

5.1 Introduction

The reasoning that is used here to understand the effects of radiation on man is based on a few simple proposals:

–   DNA is an important molecule, the integrity of which is crucial for the correct functioning of the cells in our body;

–   the correct functioning of the cells in our body is crucial for our health;

–   radiation can break the thread-like structure of the DNA;

–   these breaks lead to cellular disfunction;

–   this cellular disfunction is the source of radiation-induced health effects.

In this and the following chapters, a trail from radiation-induced damage in DNA through the cellular consequences of that damage to the occurrence of radiation-induced health effects, such as radiation sickness and cancer, will be set out. So, if you can grasp the processes described to explain how radiation induces breaks in the DNA, you will then have the basic information which will allow you to understand how radiation affects us.

It has been explained in the previous chapters that ionising radiation can break chemical bonds in molecules, that DNA is the molecule which carries the genetic information that controls the operation of all the cells in our body, that DNA is a long thread-like molecule in the form of a double helix, and that DNA forms the backbone of all of the chromosomes in the nucleus of our cells. Radiation is able to break chemical bonds in the strands of DNA and, in this chapter, the unique ability of ionising radiation to induce a complete rupture of the DNA molecule in the form of a **DNA double strand break** will be considered and explained. This double strand break in the DNA is proposed to be the critical molecular lesion which lies at the basis of all subsequent biological effects of radiation.

And the Take Home Message is:

It's the DNA double strand break that does the damage!

5.2 The Production of DNA Double Strand Breaks

The integrity of the DNA double strand molecules, which form the backbone of each of the chromosomes in the cell, is crucial for the cell to function correctly. Disruption of the DNA molecule will lead to disruption in the functioning of the cell. The crucial damage arising from radiation is a rupture of both strands of the double helix. It is a **DNA double strand break**.

In chapter 3 it was shown that radiation interaction with matter causes the ejection of electrons from molecules and the consequent rupture of chemical bonds. When this happens in the sugar-phosphate strands of the DNA molecule, the strands break. It has also been mentioned that when this occurs in water molecules, highly reactive hydroxyl radicals are created. If these hydroxyl radicals are created near to the DNA molecule, the radical attack on the strand can also result in breakage. Looking at the DNA molecule and the possible different actions of radiation, it should be clear that a radiation track may induce a break in one strand. This is a **single strand break**. Alternatively, the radiation track may cause breakage of both strands as a result of two closely spaced ionisation events along that track. This is a **double strand break**. These two types of break are shown in figure 5.1.

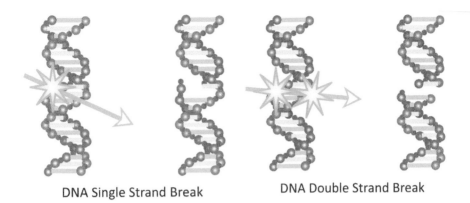

DNA Single Strand Break   DNA Double Strand Break

Figure 5.1 A pictorial representation of a radiation track inducing a single strand break in a DNA helix (left) and of a radiation track inducing a double strand break in a DNA helix (right). The ability of all ionising radiations to induce a double strand break in this way is unique.

Because the total number of tracks produced by an exposure to radiation is directly related to **radiation dose,** it is possible to quantify the production of these strand breaks. It is important to realise that both the number of single strand breaks as well as the number of double strand breaks produced by single radiation tracks are directly related to dose, although the efficiencies for each process will be different.

5.3 The Quantification of DNA Double Strand Breaks

A consideration of how DNA double strand breaks might arise as a result of radiation action reveals that there are two possible mechanisms. A double strand break may arise in the passage of one radiation track close to both strands with energy deposition (or ionisation) events close to each strand. This will be called the **'primary' mode.** Alternatively, a "first" single strand break caused by one radiation track might be converted to a double strand break by a "second" single strand break on the other strand caused by a different radiation track if the "second" break is close enough to the "first". This will be called the **'secondary' mode.** This is illustrated in figure 5.2

And the Take Home Message is:

Radiation induces a 'primary' double strand break in the passage of a single ionising track near a DNA helix. And radiation induces a 'secondary' double strand break when two ionising tracks pass close to each other near the DNA helix.

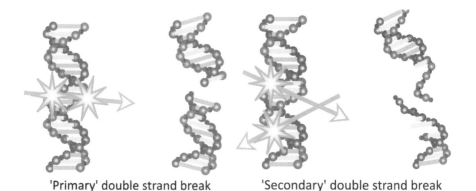

'Primary' double strand break   'Secondary' double strand break

Figure 5.2 *A pictorial representation of the induction of double strand breaks in the 'primary' mode by the passage of a single ionising track (left) and the induction of a double strand break in the 'secondary' mode by the passage of two independent ionising tracks (right).*

You can get a feel for this production of DNA double strand breaks by thinking of cutting two lengths of string with a pair of scissors. You can hold the two lengths of string together and cut both in one snip of the scissors. Both pieces of string are cut simultaneously. This is similar to the 'primary' mode of double strand break production. But you can also cut the two lengths of string separately in two snips of the scissors. In this case, the two pieces of string are not cut simultaneously. This is similar to the 'secondary' mode of double strand break production.

So, because the number of tracks produced by a radiation exposure is proportional to the radiation dose, the number of double strand breaks created by the 'primary' mode of radiation action is directly related to radiation dose. Each of the single strand breaks which combine to produce a double strand break in the 'secondary' mode of radiation action is also directly related to radiation dose. This means that the number of double strand breaks produced in the 'secondary' mode is directly related to the number of "first" single strand breaks multiplied by the number of "second" single strand breaks.

This can be written in the form of a series of simple mathematical equations by calling the dose (D), the number of 'primary' double strand breaks (N_A), the number of 'secondary' double strand breaks (N_B) and the different efficiencies for producing these breaks (*A*) and (*B*) respectively.

Now, if (*A*) is the efficiency per unit dose with which a single radiation track produces a 'primary' double strand break, then the number (N_A) of these breaks is (*A*) multiplied by dose (D). This can be written in mathematical shorthand as:

$$N_A = AD.$$

This is a "linear" function of the dose (D) and is illustrated in figure 5.3.

If (B_1) and (B_2) are the efficiencies per unit dose with which a radiation track produces a "first" or a "second" single strand break respectively, then the number (N_B) of 'secondary' double strand breaks produced is (B_1) multiplied by dose (D) multiplied by (B_2) multiplied by dose (D). This can be written in mathematical shorthand as:

$$N_B = B_1 D B_2 D \quad \text{which can be written as: } N_B = B_1 B_2 D^2.$$

This is a "quadratic" function of the dose (D) and is illustrated in figure 5.4.

[Note: D^2 means D squared, mathematical shorthand for D multiplied by itself.]

(B_1) and (B_2) have been used to represent the efficiences for the production of the "first" and "second" single strand breaks because these two efficiencies are probably different from each other.

By adding the number of 'primary' double strand breaks (N_A) to the number of 'secondary' double strand breaks (N_B), the total number (N) of double strand breaks produced by a dose (D) of radiation can be calculated to be:

$$N = N_A + N_B = AD + B_1 B_2 D^2,$$

which can be written as: $N = AD + BD^2$, where $B = B_1 B_2$. This is illustrated in figure 5.5.

This "**linear-quadratic**" equation will appear time and time again as the effects of radiation are discussed and it is just about the only equation you need to know to understand radiation health effects.

Dr Hay and Prof Dee's Take Home Message is:

'Primary' double strand breaks are directly related to radiation dose (D). 'Secondary' double strand breaks are related to radiation dose "squared" (D^2). The total number of double strand breaks is a "linear-quadratic" function of dose. This function forms the basis of all radiation health effects!

5.4   The Shape of Dose-Effect Relationships

It is reasonable to assume that (A) and (B) remain constant for an exposure to radiation. The equation $N = AD + BD^2$ can, therefore, be used to calculate the number of double strand breaks produced at different doses. We can also visualise this by making a graphical representation of the number (N) against dose (D) to produce a "**dose-effect**" relationship.

The shape of this relationship is clearer if separate graphs of the 'primary' double strand breaks (N_A) and of the 'secondary' breaks (N_B) are created before putting the two graphs together to get the total number (N).

Figure 5.3 presents a graph of 'primary' breaks (N_A) drawn against dose (D).

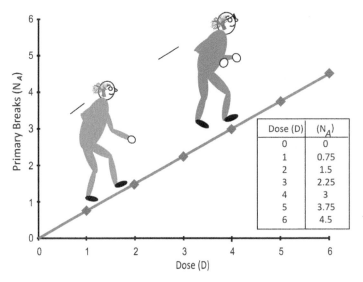

Dose (D)	(N_A)
0	0
1	0.75
2	1.5
3	2.25
4	3
5	3.75
6	4.5

Figure 5.3 *A graphical representation of the induction of 'primary' breaks as a function of dose,* $N_A = AD$ *with* $A = 0.75$. *The blue diamonds plot* (N_A) *at different doses (D) as shown in the data box. Remember the colour coding of equations and graphs!*

And, figure 5.4 presents a graph of 'secondary' breaks (N_B) against dose (D).

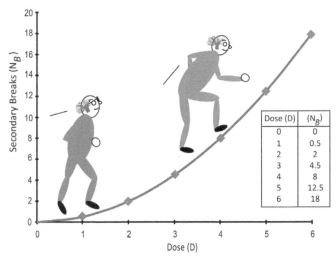

Dose (D)	(N_B)
0	0
1	0.5
2	2
3	4.5
4	8
5	12.5
6	18

Figure 5.4 *A graphical representation of the induction of 'secondary' breaks as a function of dose,* $N_B = BD^2$ *with* $B = 0.5$. *The red diamonds plot* (N_B) *at different doses (D) as shown in the data box. (Note the change of scale on the vertical 'breaks' axis from figure 5.3.)*

Figure 5.3 shows that the number of 'primary' breaks (N_A) increases in a straight line as dose (D) gets bigger. It is like a wedge with the slope equal to (A). Figure 5.4 shows that the number of 'secondary' breaks (N_B) increases slowly at first but then gets steeper and steeper as dose (D) gets bigger. In figure 5.5, these two graphs are put together to draw the total number of double strand breaks (N) against dose (D).

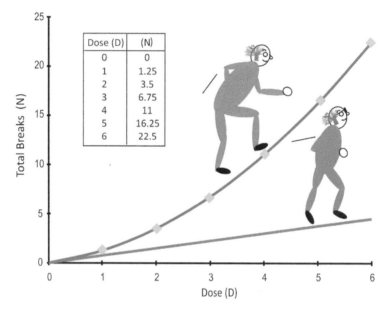

Dose (D)	(N)
0	0
1	1.25
2	3.5
3	6.75
4	11
5	16.25
6	22.5

Figure 5.5 *A graphical representation of the induction of total double strand breaks as a function of dose,* $N = AD + BD^2$ *with A = 0.75 and B = 0.5. The green diamonds plot (N) at different doses (D) as shown in the data box. Prof Dee is climbing this curve. Dr Hay is on the* $N_A = AD$ *line from figure 5.3. (Note the change of scale of the 'breaks' axis from figure 5.4 and figure 5.3.)*

Figure 5.5 shows that the total number of double strand breaks starts off in a straight line at small values of dose (D) following the number of 'primary' breaks (N_A) and with a slope of (A) as in figure 5.3. As dose (D) gets bigger, the total number of breaks curves up and away from the straight line and the number of 'secondary' breaks (N_B) becomes dominant. These three figures (5.3, 5.4 and 5.5) are, in fact, **dose-effect relationships**. At small doses, the 'primary' double strand breaks are important and the effect is defined by the value of (A). At bigger doses, the 'secondary' double strand breaks become more important.

It is essential to realise that the linear-quadratic equation is quite flexible and that the actual shape of the curve is governed by the values of (*A*) and (*B*). The general shape is, however, always similar.

In figure 5.6, a series of linear-quadratic curves has been drawn with different values of (*A*) and (*B*) to give an impression of the varying forms that the curves can take. All the curves have a straight line slope at low doses (*A*) and gradually curve up away (*B*) from that line as dose gets bigger.

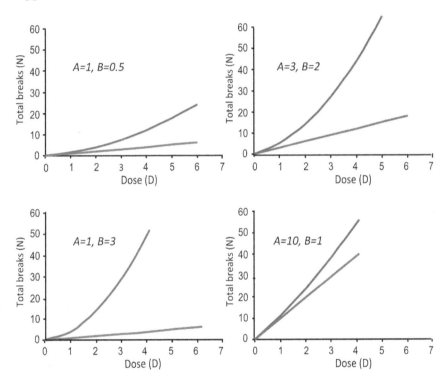

Figure 5.6 *Four illustrations of the varied shape that the linear-quadratic function can take depending on the relative values of (A) and (B).*

Figure 5.7 presents some real measurements of DNA double strand breaks induced by gamma radiation which show a similar shape of graph as that shown in figure 5.5.

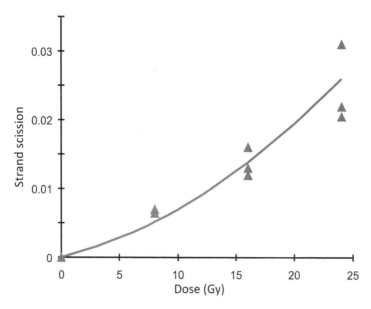

Figure 5.7 *Actual data on the induction of DNA double strand breaks by gamma-rays. The triangular data points show the usual variations in repeat experimental measurements. The curve is similar in shape to that shown in figure 5.5. Note the dose axis in units of gray (Gy) (see chapter 3).*

Although it is possible to split up the production of double strand breaks into 'primary' and 'secondary' modes mathematically, it is important to realise that neither the DNA nor the cell can distinguish between them. However, by conceptually distinguishing between them, it is possible to draw two important conclusions. One concerns the effect of the different types of radiation (alpha particles, gamma rays, etc) which influences the production of 'primary' breaks. The other concerns the effect of spreading out the accumulation of dose over long periods of time which affects the production of 'secondary' breaks. After all, everyone is exposed to different types of radiation throughout their lifetime.

5.5 The Effect of Different Types of Radiation on 'Primary' Breaks

The DNA double helix molecule is a well-defined, three dimensional, geometrical structure with known composition and dimensions and is, therefore, a specific target for radiation tracks. Figure 5.2 illustrated that 'primary' double strand breaks require the radiation track to pass close to both strands of the helix which are separated by 2 nanometers (2nm) and for the track to cause ionisation or energy deposition events close to each strand. Clearly, as radiation tracks interact with the DNA molecule from all directions, a 'wide' radiation track, depositing energy about every 2 nanometers (2nm), will have a much better chance of creating a 'primary' break than a 'very narrow' radiation track, depositing energy, say, every 5 nanometers (5nm). A pictorial representation of this is shown in figure 5.8.

A feeling for this might be gained if you imagine trying to simultaneously hit both legs of a ladder leant against a wall with water jets from different sources as you walk around the ladder at a couple of paces' distance from it. Firing a fine jet of water from a water pistol will not give many simultaneous hits on both legs but a water jet from a garden hose will improve the number of these hits. However, a water jet from a fire hose will almost always hit both legs of the ladder simultaneously.

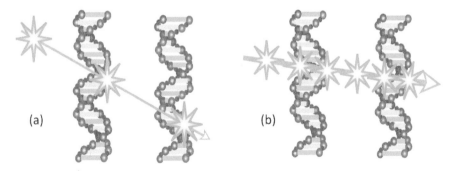

Figure 5.8 *A pictorial representation to illustrate that (a) a 'narrow' track depositing energy about every 5nm will be much less efficient at inducing 'primary' double strand breaks than (b) a 'wide' radiation track depositing energy about every 2nm.*

Gamma rays and X-rays and energetic electron tracks are like the water pistol, lower energy electron tracks and beta particles are like the garden hose and proton tracks from fast neutron radiation and alpha particles are like the fire hose.

So, alpha particles and fast neutron radiation will be very efficient in producing 'primary' breaks and have a large value of (*A*). The dose-effect relationship equation will be:

$$N = A_L D,$$

where (A_L) merely stands for a large value of (*A*). These types of radiation are called **"densely ionising"**.

One corollary of this is that, because alpha particles almost always induce 'primary' breaks, they very rarely induce 'secondary' breaks. This means that the value of (*B*) will be very small or zero for alpha radiation exposures. The same applies to a slightly lesser extent for fast neutron induced proton radiation.

Electron tracks and beta rays will be less efficient and have a smaller value of (*A*), and gamma rays and X-rays will be very inefficient producers of 'primary' tracks. These types of radiation are called **"sparsely ionising"**. In fact, it will only be the low energy electron track-ends of the secondary electrons, created by the gamma rays and X-rays as they lose their energy passing through tissue, which will create the 'primary' breaks.

It is important to recognise that, because the low energy electron track-ends are always associated with all ionising radiations and are capable of creating 'primary' double strand breaks, the value of (*A*) is never zero for any ionising radiation exposure. And, as will be seen later, this means that all exposures to any form of ionising radiation carry a health risk even though that risk might be very small.

Prof Dee and Dr Hay's Take Home Message is:

Different radiations have different efficiencies for the production of 'primary' DNA double strand breaks because they have different patterns of energy deposition. Radiation with energy depositions every 2nm or so will be a very efficient producer of 'primary' breaks.

5.6 The Effect of Spreading out the Exposure over Time on 'Secondary' Breaks

It should be clear from figure 5.2 that the two breaks created by a single radiation track which make a 'primary' double strand break are simultaneous in time. It should also be clear that the two single strand breaks created by two independent radiation tracks to form a 'secondary' double strand break are not simultaneous in time. This can be seen by returning to the analogy of cutting the two lengths of string with scissors. When each length of string is cut separately in two snips there is always one piece cut first and then, a little later, the second piece. It is the same when the double strand break is produced in the 'secondary' mode by the combination of two single strand breaks. If the exposure occurs over a short period of time, then the two breaks must occur within that time. However, if the exposure is spread out over a longer period, then it is quite possible that the "first" single strand break might be hanging around for some time before it is converted to a 'secondary' double strand break by the "second" single strand break. And, if the first single strand break can be repaired, it will not be there any more to be converted to a double strand break when the second radiation track arrives. The consequence of spreading out the exposure over time is thus a reduction of the value of (B). Indeed, if the exposure is spread out over several hours, the repair of the 'first' single strand breaks can be complete so that the value of (B) becomes zero. Only the 'primary' breaks remain and the radiation effect reduces to the simple linear equation:

$$N = AD.$$

In fact, the repair of single strand breaks is well documented in scientific literature. The cell carries the DNA replication machinery (the enzymes), the undamaged strand is copied and the repair is perfect.

The decrease in the number of DNA double strand breaks when the exposure is spread out over a few hours and (B) reduces to zero, is normally called the "dose-rate effect". It is crucially important when radiation risk is assessed because the risk of a health effect arising from a "protracted" exposure of, for instance, gamma rays, is far less than the risk from a short-term or "acute" exposure.

For radiations, such as alpha particles and fast neutron-induced proton radiation, which are so efficient at producing 'primary' double strand breaks that they produce very few 'secondary' breaks, this "dose-rate effect" is hardly found. Even in an acute exposure to these densely ionising radiations, the value of (B) is expected to be very small or zero.

Although it might be difficult to imagine that radiation damage can be repaired, if it is explained step by step, it should become clear. In chapter 3, you have seen that radiation interacts with the electrons of molecules to break the chemical bonds holding the molecules together. When this happens at a strand of the DNA, the radiation causes a break in that strand. A radiation-induced single strand break amounts, therefore, to a gap along one strand of the double helix even though the other strand is not damaged. Because the integrity of the DNA is crucial for the cell, the DNA is constantly monitored for damage and the single strand gap is rapidly recognised. The undamaged strand holds the DNA together and provides the template of nucleotide bases for repair. Just as in DNA replication, there are enzymes which attach the correct complementary nucleotide base to each nucleotide base on the intact strand, adenine (A) with thymine (T) and cytosine (C) with guanine (G), and thus restore the double stranded DNA (see figure 5.9). In this way, the cell can ensure the complete and perfect repair of all radiation-induced single strand breaks, if it is given enough time.

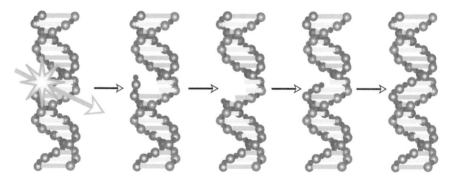

Figure 5.9 *A pictorial representation of how a DNA single strand break can be perfectly repaired.*

In fact, as will be seen later, the cell is also able to repair radiation-induced DNA double strand breaks, although this process cannot be guaranteed to give a perfect repair every time.

Dr Hay and Prof Dee's Take Home Message is:

The two single strand breaks which make a 'secondary' double strand break are independent of each other in time. The cell can repair the 'first' single strand break perfectly, if it is given enough time. When the exposure to radiation is spread out over a few hours, this repair of the 'first' single strand breaks reduces the number of 'secondary' double strand breaks, eventually, to zero. This is the dose-rate effect and is important for gamma ray, X-ray and beta particle exposures.

5.7 Summary

It has been shown that the induction of DNA double strand breaks can be described by a "linear-quadratic" function of dose:

$$N = AD + BD^2.$$

This function can be represented graphically by a curve which starts at zero dose with a linear slope defined by (A) and then curves upwards as (B) becomes more important.

It has also been shown that the value of (A) is never zero for any type of ionising radiation. The value of (A) depends on the type of radiation and the pattern of ionisation events at the nanometer scale near the DNA molecules. Densely ionising alpha particle tracks will be much more efficient at producing 'primary' double strand breaks and have a larger value of (A) than the sparsely ionising gamma rays and X-rays.

However, in a short exposure, sparsely ionising radiation will produce many 'secondary' double strand breaks as the dose increases. If the exposure to sparsely ionising radiation is protracted over several hours, the repair of "first" single strand breaks, before they are converted to double strand breaks, leads to a reduction of the value of (*B*). And the dose-rate effect can eventually lead to (*B*) becoming zero.

All this is shown graphically in figure 5.10.

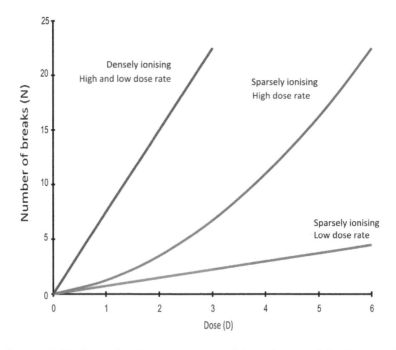

Figure 5.10 *A graphical representation of the induction of double strand breaks by high and low dose rates of densely ionising and sparsely ionising radiations.*

It is important to be aware that both the value of (*A*) and the value of (*B*) are influenced by the conditions pertaining when exposure occurs. As an example, exposure in an oxygen poor environment causes less radiation damage than when exposure occurs in an oxygen rich environment.

CHAPTER 6

Cellular Effects of Radiation

6.1 Introduction

This chapter will describe the cellular effects of radiation because they are the source of both the short-term and the long-term health effects of radiation. Once the background and the cause of the cellular effects have been grasped, it will be rather straightforward to understand how the health effects arise.

There are three different radiation-induced effects that can be measured experimentally and used to assess cellular damage. These three effects are:

–   **chromosome structural changes,** arising from a backbone break,
–   **mutations,** when the genetic make-up of surviving cells is permanently altered,
–   **cell killing,** when the exposed cells are unable to continue dividing.

Radiation-induced chromosome structural changes, or **chromosomal aberrations,** will be used first to explain the action of radiation on the cell because their association with DNA double strand breaks is the most straightforward. However, it should become clear that each of the three effects, cell killing, mutations and chromosomal aberrations can all be related to the same radiation-induced molecular lesion, the DNA double strand break. The scheme for this is shown in figure 6.1

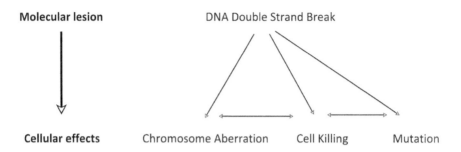

Figure 6.1 *A simple diagram of the pathway from the radiation-induced molecular lesion, i.e. DNA double strand breaks, to the three different cellular effects: chromosome aberrations, cell killing and mutations.*

6.2 Radiation-Induced Chromosomal Aberrations

In section 4.2, you learnt that the nucleus of a human cell contains 22 pairs of homologous chromosomes plus the 2 sex chromosomes. In the G_1 cell phase, each chromosome has a single DNA double helix molecule as its backbone so that a radiation-induced DNA double strand break is, in fact, a break in the chromosome backbone. In the G_2 cell phase, the DNA double strand break causes a chromatid arm break. These breaks lead to structural changes in the chromosomes (chromosomal aberrations) which can be seen and counted in the microscope almost immediately after radiation exposure. The number of aberrations per cell can be used to measure the radiation damage to the cell.

After a radiation exposure of cells, which might be plant root tips, blood lymphocytes or tissue cells in culture, the cells can be gathered at the first cell division (mitosis) when the chromosomes have contracted and can be examined using a microscope. The chromosomes can be stained and even individually identified. Any structural differences found in chromosomes in irradiated cells compared with those in unirradiated cells can be counted. There is a wide variety of structural differences and figure 6.2 presents two of the more common ones.

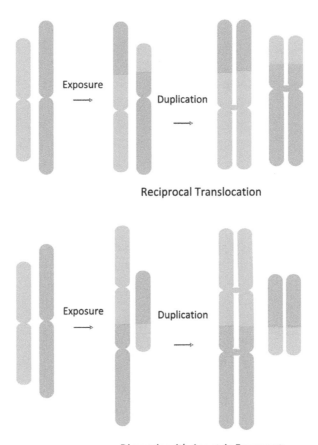

Reciprocal Translocation

Dicentric with Acentric Fragment

Figure 6.2 *A pictorial representation of two typical chromosomal aberrations found after radiation exposure. The reciprocal translocation (upper picture) results from an exchange of pieces of chromosome arms between two chromosomes. The dicentric (lower picture) has two centromeres and is accompanied by a composite piece of chromosome without a centromere. Both pictures show two chromosomes (one blue, one pink) before exposure with what results and what is seen in the microscope at mitosis after the aberrations have gone through chromosome duplication.*

Even though figure 6.2 appears to show two chromosome backbone breaks, the model for chromosome aberration formation used here proposes that these chromosomal aberrations arise from only one radiation-induced DNA double strand break (a single chromosome backbone break) and that the second break arises as a result of the cell's attempt to repair that radiation-induced double strand break.

The inspiration for this process of chromosomal aberration formation is derived from a proposal made in 1976 by an American scientist, Mike Resnick. Resnick suggested that DNA double strand breaks might be rather well repaired by a process of "crossing-over", or "recombination", similar to a biological process well known to occur in reproductive cells when they go through the meiotic cycle. In one stage of meiosis, the maternal and paternal homologous chromosomes pair together and a process of "crossing over" or "homologous recombination" occurs. This shuffles some of the paternal DNA into the maternal DNA and vice versa which contributes to genetic diversity in the following generation.

Resnick proposed that a double strand break in a chromosome could be properly repaired if a **template** were used so that the complete gap in the double helix backbone could be correctly copied. This is a little bit like the perfect repair of DNA single strand breaks. That template, Resnick suggested, would be provided by the homologous chromosome, the undamaged partner of the broken chromosome. The nice thing about Resnick's proposal is that his repair model makes use of all the enzymes and DNA base pairing known from the repair of single strand breaks together with the "crossing-over" process known in meiosis. Resnick's repair process is illustrated in figure 6.3.

The extension that was made to apply Resnick's DNA repair model to the formation of chromosomal aberrations was the proposal that the large amounts of 'repetitive' DNA, found scattered throughout all the chromosomes, could provide small regions of DNA that were homologous with the broken DNA where repair could take place. These small regions of homology, or identical DNA base sequences, are not necessarily on the homologous chromosomes. It was found that, if the "crossing-over" process occurred at these regions on different chromosomes and, if the resolution of the crossing-over was not always correct, then a whole series of different structural changes to the chromosomes could arise from the cell's attempt to repair the radiation-induced double strand break. An example is illustrated in figure 6.4.

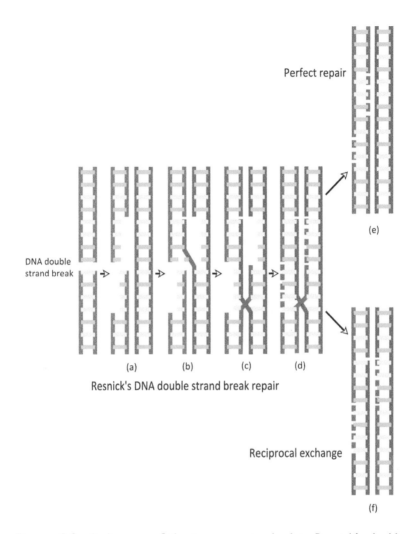

Figure 6.3 A diagram of the processes involved in Resnick's double strand break 'crossing-over' repair. (a) At the double strand break, enzymes create two single strand tails. These tails (red) find a homologous unbroken DNA helix (blue) with the same base pair sequence and the 'crossing-over' repair commences. (b) One strand from the undamaged helix pairs with one of the single strand tails using complementary base matching. (c) Unwinding of the undamaged helix (blue) allows the second single strand tail (red) to pair with it. (d) This leads to two single strand gaps which can be repaired (chopped red strands) by using the base sequences on the two (blue) strands of the undamaged homologous DNA helix. Please note that there are two possible results depending on how the 'crossing-over' unravels: (e) perfect repair or (f) reciprocal exchange between the two DNA helices (blue to red and vice versa).

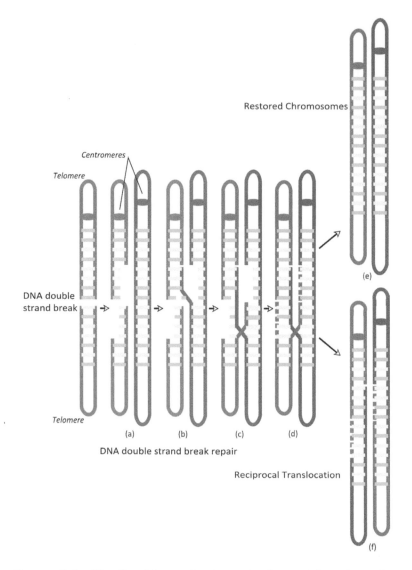

Restored Chromosomes

Centromeres

Telomere

DNA double
strand break

Telomere

(a)   (b)   (c)   (d)

DNA double strand break repair

Reciprocal Translocation

(e)

(f)

Figure 6.4 *The Resnick repair, shown in figure 6.3, converted to chromosome view but with two non-homologous chromosomes (red and blue). The steps (a), (b), (c) and (d) are exactly the same as shown in figure 6.3. Depending on the unravelling of the 'cross-over', either (e) restored chromosomes result (upper) or (f) the reciprocal exchange leads to a reciprocal translocation aberration, blue end to red chromosome and vice versa (lower) (see figure 6.2). The upper arms of the chromosomes have been drawn short for convenience. Note: If the blue chromosome had its centromere at the bottom, instead of at the top, the aberration formed would be a dicentric (see figure 6.2).*

All the different structural changes which could be designed via this type of repair process conform precisely with all the different types of chromosomal aberrations measured in cells after radiation exposure.

Figure 6.4 reveals that the Resnick repair of a radiation-induced double strand break leads to one of two results depending on the unravelling of the cross-over. Correct resolution of the cross-over leads to restored chromosomes with no apparent damage. Incorrect resolution of the cross-over leads to an exchange between the two chromosomes of parts of their arms. This results in what appear to be two broken chromosome arms. The Resnick repair provides a process to explain that chromosomal aberrations arise from a single radiation-induced break in one chromosome backbone which leads, during the cell's attempt to repair that break, to a second chromosome break that is **not** radiation-induced. The second break arises during the incorrect resolution of the crossing-over repair process.

So, even though figure 6.2 shows two chromosome backbone breaks, one is radiation-induced and the other is a consequence of the repair process.

This is one important feature of the model used here which contradicts the current radiobiological dogma.

But Our Take Home Message is:

Chromosome aberrations arise from a single chromosome backbone break, ie. a DNA double strand break. This is a consequence of Resnick's double strand break 'cross-over' repair process combined with repetitive DNA scattered throughout the chromosomes.

Now, if the number of chromosomal aberrations is measured after different levels of exposure, or different radiation doses, the number of chromosomal aberrations counted at each dose level can be plotted against the level of dose to create a **dose-effect relationship.**

A typical example of such a dose-effect relationship with experimental data is shown in figure 6.5 and it is clear that the line drawn through the data has the same sort of 'linear-quadratic' shape as was derived for DNA double strand breaks.

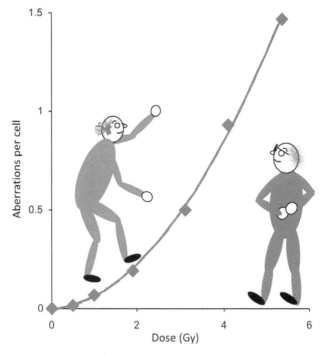

Figure 6.5 *A graphical representation of a dose-effect relationship for chromosome aberrations. The diamonds are real data measured in blood lymphocytes. The red line through the diamonds is indeed a 'linear-quadratic' equation. Note the dose axis in units of gray (Gy) (see chapter 3).*

If the chromosomal aberrations are indeed derived from DNA double strand breaks, then it can be expected that the yield of aberrations (Y), that is, the average number of aberrations per cell, will be equal to the number of DNA double strand breaks (N) multiplied by the chance (c) that a double strand break forms an observable chromosomal aberration, so that:

$$Y = cN = c(AD + BD^2).$$

[Remember the colour coding of equations and lines in graphs.]

At very low doses, the graph is dominated by the value of (*A*) for the production of 'primary' double strand breaks but at larger doses it curves upwards as the 'secondary' breaks increase in importance. The equations can be fitted to the experimental data by statistically optimising the values of (*A*) and (*B*).

By doing similar experiments under different exposure conditions, a series of dose-effect relationships can be made to map the changing radiation effects. In this way, a study can be made, for example, of whether the effects of different radiation types or the protraction of radiation exposure conform with the expectations that were outlined in sections 5.4 and 5.5.

[Note that in all the following dose-effect graphs, in addition to the colour coding of equations and lines, the colour red will be reserved for the results of an acute exposure to sparsely ionising radiation, such as gamma or X-rays, green will be reserved for the results of an exposure to densely ionising radiation, such as alpha particles or protons from fast neutrons, and **blue** for the results of protracted low dose-rate exposure to sparsely ionising radiation.]

Measurements of chromosomal aberrations induced in mammalian cells can be made in the laboratory by using blood samples or by using human and animal cells in cell cultures. These are much more simple to measure than DNA double strand breaks. Consequently, there is a vast scientific data base available on chromosomal aberrations.

Figure 6.6 shows some of the results from this data base to demonstrate that, as expected, different types of radiation do produce different dose-effect relationships. The more vigorously ionising radiations (densely ionising) do have steeper curves with larger (*A*) values and the curves are more linear.

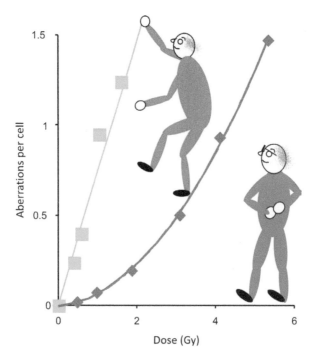

Figure 6.6 *A graphical representation of the dose-effect relationship for chromosome aberrations induced by densely ionising radiation (fast neutrons, green curve) compared with the red curve from figure 6.5 for sparsely ionising radiation. The green curve is essentially linear and is dominated by a large value of (A). The green squares are real data measured in blood lymphocytes.*

The next figure, 6.7, demonstrates the effect that extending the time of radiation exposure to the same doses, from a few minutes to several hours or days, has on the shape of the dose-effect relationship of sparsely ionising radiations. The figure shows that the curvature decreases with longer exposure times and that, eventually, the value of (*B*) will become zero. This is because the cell is able to repair DNA single strand breaks perfectly during the longer exposure time. At this stage the dose-effect relationship reduces to the linear equation:

$$Y = c\mathcal{A}D.$$

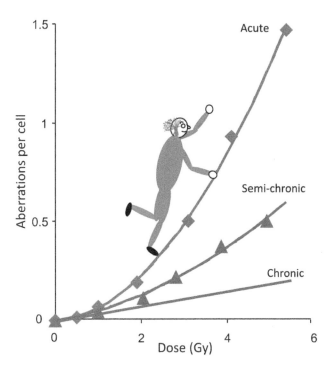

Figure 6.7 *A graphical representation of the consequence of protracting the exposure to sparsely ionising radiation on the dose-effect relationship. The number of chromosome aberrations measured decreases as exposure lengthens because (B) becomes smaller. Eventually, the number of aberrations found for long exposures (blue curve) is defined only by the value of (A). The diamonds and triangles are real data measured in blood lymphocytes.*

And Our Take Home Message is:

Chromosome aberration dose-effect curves are generally 'linear-quadratic'. Densely ionising radiations have a larger (A) value and almost 'linear' curves. The induction of aberrations by sparsely ionising radiations is substantially reduced by extending exposure time, that is, by reducing dose rate.

This means that at quite low doses for either a short-term, acute exposure or a longer-term, protracted or chronic exposure, the radiation effect is defined by the value of (A) for the induction of 'primary' double strand breaks. And at higher doses for longer-term, protracted exposures, the radiation effect is also defined by the value of (A). This is important and implies that it is the value of (A) for the induction of 'primary' DNA double strand breaks that governs the health risks of ionising radiations for the radiation protection of the general public.

6.3 Radiation-Induced Mutations

As the DNA backbones of the chromosomes carry all the genes that control the normal function of the cell, it is reasonable to assume that any disruption of the genetic integrity of the DNA might lead to an alteration in the genes and the induction of a mutation. We have seen that a DNA single strand break can be repaired perfectly through the copying of the undamaged strand so a single strand break will not cause a mutation. A DNA double strand break, however, cannot always be repaired perfectly, does cause a disruption of the mechanical integrity of the DNA and can clearly lead to an alteration in the DNA genetic code and thus cause a mutation.

This section concentrates on the induction of mutations in the somatic cells of normal tissue which can be detected in human or animal cell cultures in the laboratory. These methods make use of a selective chemical to detect the mutated cells capable of growing in a culture medium containing that chemical. The methods detect the frequency of mutations (M) occurring in cells which survive the radiation exposure.

A substantial scientific data base of experiments on the induction of somatic mutations in human and animal cells has been developed. Figure 6.8 presents a typical dose-effect curve for the induction of mutations in animal cells after gamma ray exposure and shows the same upward curvature with increasing dose found for chromosome aberrations (see fig 6.5).

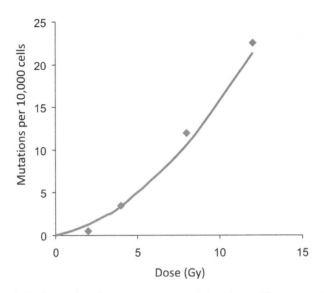

Figure 6.8 *A graphical representation of the dose-effect curve for the induction of mutations by sparsely ionising radiation. The red line drawn through the data is, indeed, a linear-quadratic equation.*

The line drawn through the data is the now familiar linear-quadratic function and the frequency of mutations per surviving cell (M) can be equated to the number (N) of double strand breaks and, consequently, to radiation dose (D) by the equation:

$$M = q(N) = q(AD + BD^2),$$

where (q) is the chance that a DNA double strand break leads to the specific mutation studied. The value of (q) is very small because it is related to the very small amount of DNA in the cell which governs the expression of the specific mutation. That is why the number of mutations is measured in such a large population (10,000) of cells (see figure 6.8).

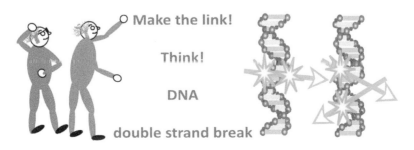

Figure 6.9 presents data for the induction of mutations following exposure to densely ionising radiation together with the data for sparsely ionising radiation taken from figure 6.8 and shows that the induction of somatic mutations behaves in a comparable way to the induction of chromosomal aberrations (see fig 6.6). The dose-effect curve becomes more linear with a larger value of (*A*) when more densely ionising radiation is used to irradiate the cells.

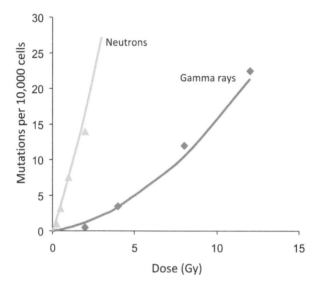

Figure 6.9 A graphical representation of the dose-effect relationship for mutations induced by densely ionising radiation (green curve) compared with the red curve from figure 6.8 for sparsely ionising radiation. The green curve is steeper, essentially linear and dominated by a large value of (A).

Figure 6.10 shows the same effect of dose-rate reduction (or extension of exposure time) to sparsely ionising radiation on the frequency of mutations as was found for chromosomal aberrations (see fig 6.7). The frequency of mutations decreases as the exposure times increase until the value of (*B*) becomes zero and the dose-effect relationship reduces to the linear equation:

$$M = qAD.$$

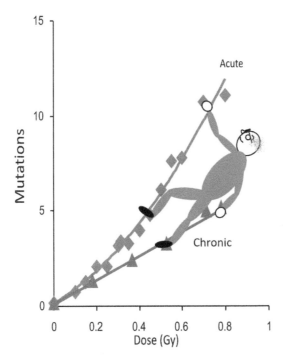

Figure 6.10 *A graphical representation of the effect of protracting exposure over time. The number of mutations measured decreases as exposure lengthens because (B) becomes smaller. Eventually, the number of mutations found for long exposures is defined by the value of (A). The diamonds and triangles are real data measured in Tradescantia stamen hairs. This system is interesting because it allows mutations to be measured after quite small radiation doses (see Dose axis).*

Again, it is important to realise that at low doses for either a short-term, acute exposure or a longer-term, protracted exposure, and at higher doses for longer-term, protracted exposures, the induction of mutations is dependent only on the value of (*A*). This is essential for radiation protection and implies that it is the value of (*A*) for the induction of 'primary' DNA double strand breaks that governs the health risks of ionising radiations for the general public.

And the Take Home Message is:

Well, it's the same as the previous one except it applies to mutations this time. Dose-effect curves are 'linear-quadratic' in general but densely ionising radiations have a larger (A) value for primary lesions. The induction of mutations by sparsely ionising radiations is substantially reduced by reducing dose rate. Things are beginning to look familiar!

At this point, it is necessary to explain that, in the case of mutations, the equations just used are not quite complete although they are accurate at low mutation frequencies. Clearly, a cell can only be mutated, say from red to magenta, once. This means that the maximum number of red to magenta mutations per cell can never exceed the value 1. However, the approximate equation used until now for mutations, namely $M = q(AD + BD^2)$, can exceed the value 1 and needs a slight modification so that the full and proper equation for the mutation frequency per surviving cell becomes:

$$M = 1 - \exp\{-q(N)\} = 1 - \exp\{-q(AD + BD^2)\}.$$

Please remember that $\exp(0) = 1$ so that, when $N = AD + BD^2 = 0$ at zero dose, $M = 1 - \exp(0) = 0$ and, at large values of $q(N)$ the value of $[\exp\{-q(N)\}]$ approaches zero, so that, at higher doses, M approaches the value 1 (see ch. 2, end section 2.2).

The magenta equation starts with $M = 0$ at zero dose, curves linear-quadratically upwards but turns flatter to saturate with $M = 1$ at higher doses. It can never exceed the value 1, where, in a population of cells this would mean that all the cells (100%) were mutated.

Figure 6.11 presents a graph of the two equations for (M) and shows that the approximate equation and the accurate equation are the same at values of (M) below 0.2 mutations per cell. Only at values of (M) above 0.25 do the curves of the two equations deviate and the magenta curve (associated with the magenta equation) saturates at the value 1. All the data in figures 6.8, 6.9 and 6.10 are well below the value of

0.2 mutations per cell, so the use of the approximate equation in those figures is appropriate.

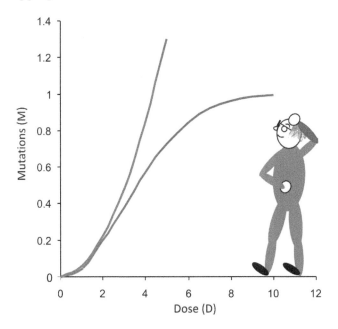

Figure 6.11 *A graphical comparison of the approximate (red) equation for mutations and the full (magenta) equation which saturates at the value of 1. The approximate equation (red curve) gives a good representation of the mutation curve up to a value of 0.2 mutations.*

6.4 Hereditary Effects

One of the health effects of radiation exposure mentioned at the beginning of the book was "Hereditary Effects". These effects arise in the next or following generations of exposed parents as a consequence of radiation damage in the reproductive or germ cells. The first evidence for radiation-induced hereditary effects was found in 1927 when hereditable mutations were found in the offspring of irradiated fruit flies (Drosophila).

In section 6.2, the induction of DNA double strand breaks was associated with the occurrence of mutations. However, the mutations considered in section 6.2 and, indeed, the data used in figures 6.8, 6.9 and 6.10, concerned mutations occurring in irradiated normal somatic cells and not in reproductive cells. It is but a further logical step to associate radiation-induced DNA double strand breaks with heritable mutations induced in reproductive or germ cells. Nevertheless, the biology of reproduction is somewhat more complicated than the straightforward mitotic division of a somatic cell.

There have been extensive studies of radiation effects on reproductive cells that have involved exposures of small animals (mice) or fruit flies (drosophila). These studies have shown that radiation can induce mutations in the offspring and that the dose-effect relationships are generally linear-quadratic. In addition, the effects of different types of radiation and the effect of reduced dose rate are directly comparable with the mutations induced in normal somatic cells and imply that hereditary mutations also arise from DNA double strand breaks.

In spite of the more complicated biology, it can be concluded that "Hereditary Effects" arise as a cellular response and that the reasoning that has been applied to both chromosomal aberrations and somatic mutations will also apply to hereditary mutations. Therefore, it can be anticipated that at low doses for either a short-term, acute exposure or a longer-term, protracted exposure, and at higher doses for longer-term, protracted exposures, the induction of "Hereditary Effects" will be dependent only on the value of (A) for the production of 'primary' double strand breaks.

In other words, at low dose and at low dose rates, "Hereditary Effects" will increase in proportion with radiation dose. However, there are no good human data to indicate how steep that increase will be except that the survey of the atomic bomb survivors is, so far, rather reassuring and suggests that it will not be very large.

This is important for radiation protection and implies that it is the value of (A) for the induction of 'primary' DNA double strand breaks that governs the "Hereditary Effects" risks of ionising radiations for the general public.

6.5   Cell Killing and Cell Survival

It is now possible to derive an equation for radiation-induced cell killing. This is done by associating a lethal mutation with the cell killing and using the same type of equation as was used for somatic mutations. This time, the full and proper equation must be used because a cell is either killed or not. So, if (p) is the chance that a DNA double strand break causes cell killing (K) then:

$$K = 1 - \exp\{-p(N)\} = 1 - \exp\{-p(AD + BD^2)\}.$$

Actually, in practice, cultures of cells are plated on growth medium after exposure and the number of growing cells, which form visible colonies, is determined so that cell survival (S) is experimentally measured. Cell survival is the opposite of cell killing and is given by the equation:

$$S = 1 - K = \exp\{-p(N)\} = \exp\{-p(AD + BD^2)\}.$$

Figure 6.12 presents a graph of this red equation with dose (D) on the horizontal axis of the graph and cell survival (S) on the vertical axis. This vertical axis has a logarithmic scale decreasing in decades to accommodate the exponential nature of the survival equation. Some actual cell survival data are also shown in the graph.

The red equation actually represents the chance that a single cell survives and you will remember that 'exp(0) = 1' (see ch. 2, end section 2.2), so cell survival starts at the value 1 at zero dose. Applied to a population of cells, this means that 100% of the cells survive at zero dose. As dose increases, the chance that the single cell survives decreases and that translates to a reduction in the percentage of cells in a population that survive. This is why 100%, 10% and 1% have been written next to the values 1, 0.1 and 0.01 on the cell survival axis. The percentages give the proportion of cells in the exposed population which will survive. It should be clear that the mirror drawn at the top of the figure of survival reflects the same sort of linear-quadratic shape as we have seen for chromosomal aberrations and mutations (figures 6.5 and 6.8).

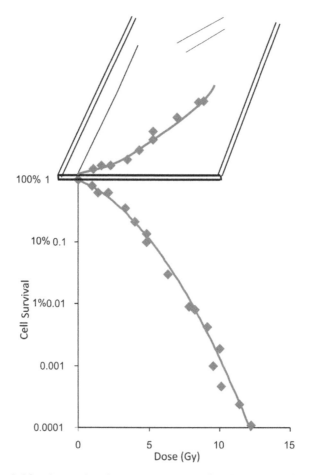

Figure 6.12 *A graphical representation of cell survival drawn on a logarithmic scale against dose on a normal scale. The red line is drawn using the red linear-quadratic survival equation. The diamonds are actual data points. The mirror drawn above the graph is there to show that cell survival looks just like a mirror image of the dose-effect curves for chromosome aberrations and mutations as shown in figures 6.5 and 6.8.*

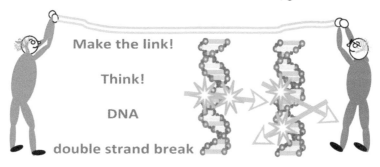

Make the link!

Think!

DNA

double strand break

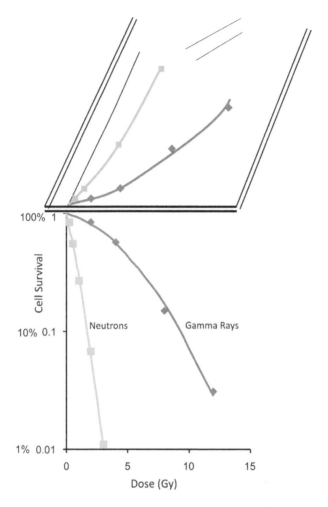

Figure 6.13 *A graphical representation of the dose-effect curve for cell survival induced by densely ionising radiation (green curve) compared with that for sparsely ionising radiation (red curve). The green curve is essentially linear and is dominated by a large value of (A). The mirror image shows the comparable behaviour of cell survival to that for aberrations and mutations shown in figures 6.6 and 6.9.*

Figure 6.13 presents data showing that cell survival after exposure to densely ionising radiation behaves in a comparable way to the induction of chromosomal aberrations and mutations (see figures 6.6 and 6.9). The dose-effect curve becomes more linear with a larger value of (*A*) when more densely ionising radiation is used to irradiate the cells.

Figure 6.14 shows the same effect of dose-rate reduction of sparsely ionising radiation on cell survival as was found for chromosomal aberrations and mutations (see figures 6.7 and 6.10). As the level of cell killing decreases, more cells survive, and the curve becomes more linear as the dose rate decreases and exposure times increase. The value of (B) becomes zero and the dose-effect relationship becomes:

$$S = \exp\{-p(AD)\}.$$

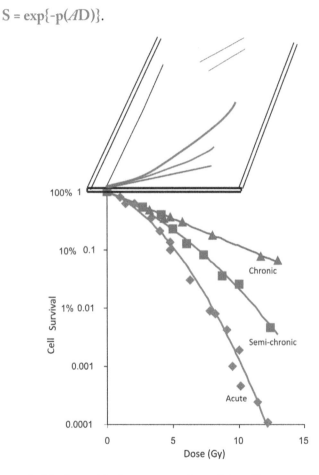

Figure 6.14 *A graphical representation of the effect on cell survival of extending the exposure time. At longer exposure times, more cells survive and the radiation effect decreases until, at chronic exposures, it becomes only defined by the value of (A). The straight blue line represents the blue equation. The red diamonds, magenta squares and blue triangles represent real data. The mirror reveals a mirror image and is similar to the effects for chromosomal aberrations and mutations shown in figures 6.7 and 6.10.*

So Our Take Home Message is:

Once you get the idea of the mirror image, radiation effects on survival begin to look very familiar and similar to the picture for aberrations and mutations. It's all beginning to come together.

Once more, it needs to be stressed that at low doses for either a short-term, acute exposure or a longer-term, protracted exposure, and at higher doses for a longer-term, protracted exposure, the killing of cells is dependent only on the value of (*A*). This is important for radiation protection and implies that it is the value of (*A*) for the induction of 'primary' DNA double strand breaks that governs the risks of ionising radiations for the general public.

And the Important Take Home Message is:

The value of (A), that governs the efficiency of radiations to produce primary DNA double strand breaks, is crucially important for the radiation protection of us all.

6.6 Interrelationships

The figures presented above demonstrate that, in practice, all three of the cellular effects of radiation have the same linear-quadratic dose-effect relationship and show similar responses to more densely ionising radiations and to a decrease in dose rate. This supports the assumption that a common molecular lesion, a DNA double strand break, can cause each cellular effect and supports the scheme of the model shown in figure 6.1. However, the scheme of the model also anticipates interrelationships between the different cellular effects (see horizontal arrows in figure 6.1). These interrelationships can be investigated when two of the cellular effects, for example, aberrations and survival, are measured together in the same batch of exposed cells. When this is done for batches of cells exposed to a series of different radiation doses the data allows directly comparable dose-effect relationships for each of the two cellular effects to be measured. It also allows the direct comparison of how the two cellular effects change with dose. This is achieved when the series of measurements of the two cellular effects are used to create a graph showing how cell survival varies as the number of aberrations increases. The investigation of interrelatedness becomes more scientifically rigorous when different exposure conditions are used to give different dose-effect relationships.

There are several data sets available in the scientific literature which permit the study of the interrelatedness of both chromosomal aberrations and cell survival and also mutations and cell survival. The interrelationship between the two effects can be examined by graphically plotting the one effect value against the other effect value at each of the doses used. If all the data from the different doses and exposure conditions lie close together along a straight line, then we can say that the two cellular effects (aberrations and survival or mutations and survival) are, indeed, interrelated. The two effects are said to be 'correlated' with each other. On the other hand, if the data do not all lie along the same straight line, then there is no correlation between the two effects.

Some data will now be presented to support the scheme shown in figure 6.1. Figure 6.15 presents data from the 1970s which show, on the left, two different dose-effect curves for chromosomal aberrations and cell survival, measured together in the same experiments but made under different exposure conditions. On the right, the single, common, straight line interrelationship between the two cellular effects is shown. This figure implies that the curvature of the chromosomal aberration yield is perfectly reflected by the curvature of the cell survival and that the interrelationship between the two effects is independent of the values of (A) and (B) which govern that curvature.

The simple interpretation of the red straight line in figure 6.15 is that aberrations cause cell killing. The interpretation preferred here goes a little deeper and is that both cell killing and aberrations are caused by similar lesions which are DNA double strand breaks.

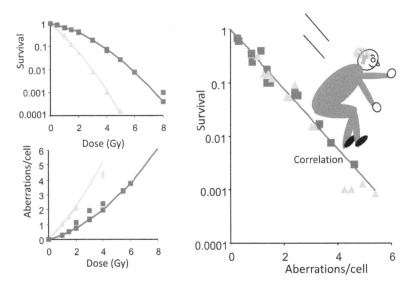

Figure 6.15 *The left hand side of the figure presents dose-effect curves made under different exposure conditions for cell survival and for chromosome aberrations measured together. Both survival and aberrations show the typical linear-quadratic curvature in each dose-effect relationship. On the right hand side of the figure, the relationship between survival and aberrations is examined and the aberrations per cell are drawn against the corresponding cell survival (on logarithmic scale) at each dose level. The straight red line through all the data indicates that the curvature of the survival mimics exactly the curvature of the aberrations and this is called a 'correlation'. The magenta squares and turquoise triangles are real data.*

Figure 6.16 presents similar data from the 1980s for mutation frequency and cell survival with the single, common, straight line interrelationship between these two cellular effects. This figure implies that the curvature of the mutation frequency is reflected by the curvature of the cell survival and that the interrelationship between the two effects is independent of the values of (*A*) and (*B*) which govern that curvature.

The preferred interpretation of the correlation is that cell killing and mutations are both caused by DNA double strand breaks.

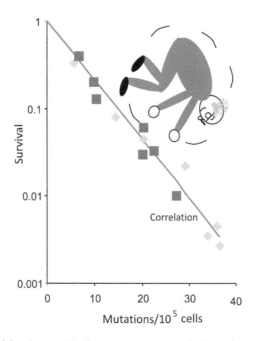

Figure 6.16 *A graphical representation of the relationship between survival and mutations, drawing the mutations against the corresponding survival (on logarithmic scale) for each dose from experiments made under two different exposure conditions. The straight red line through all the data indicates that the curvature of the survival mimics exactly the curvature of the mutations and this is called a 'correlation'. The magenta squares and turquoise diamonds are real data.*

Figure 6.17 presents some data from the 1990s for the induction of DNA double strand breaks and cell survival measured together under different experimental conditions (upper graphs). The single, common, straight line interrelationship which connects the DNA double strand breaks to cell survival is drawn in the lower graph. This figure, taken together with the previous two figures, implies that the DNA double strand break is the common molecular lesion which is the origin of each of the cellular effects: aberrations, mutations and cell survival.

Forgive us, but this is our BIG SMILER:

DNA double strand breaks are correlated with cell survival! And cell survival is correlated with aberrations and mutations!

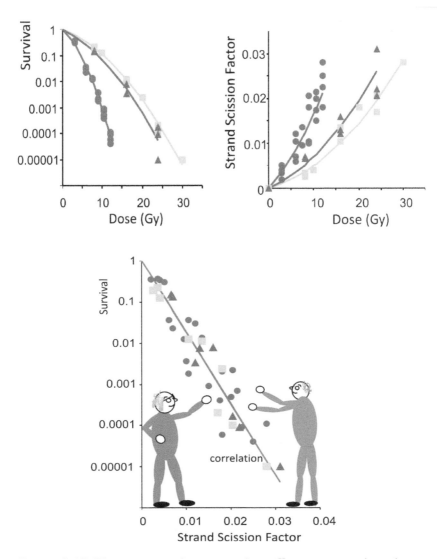

Figure 6.17 *The upper graphs present dose-effect curves made under different exposure conditions for cell survival and for the induction of DNA double strand breaks (strand scission factor) measured together. Both survival and double strand breaks show the typical linear-quadratic curvature for each dose-effect relationship. In the lower graph, the interrelationship is examined by plotting the induction of double strand breaks against cell survival (on logarithmic scale) at each dose point. The straight red line through all the data indicates that the curvature of survival mimics exactly the curvature of the double strand breaks and demonstrates a correlation between them. The magenta circles, turquoise squares and blue triangles are real data.*

The more mathematically inclined reader will be able to derive the equations for these common interrelationships by replacing N in the cell survival equation with the appropriate equivalent for chromosomal aberration yield (Y) or the approximate equivalent for mutation frequency (M) to obtain:

$S = \exp\{-pY/c\}$, which says that, if survival is plotted on a logarithmic scale against chromosomal aberration yield, a straight line relationship will be found (see red line correlation in figure 6.15), and:

$S = \exp\{-pM/q\}$, which says that, if survival is plotted on a logarithmic scale against mutation frequency, a straight line relationship will be found (see red line correlation in figure 6.16).

The relationship between DNA double strand breaks and cell survival is, of course, given by:

$S = \exp\{-p(N)\}$, which says that, if survival is plotted on a logarithmic scale against the number of double strand breaks, a straight line relationship will be found (see red line correlation in figure 6.17).

Each of these linear relationships is independent of the curvature of the dose-effect relationships, as defined by the value of (A) and (B), for chromosomal aberration yield, mutation frequency or DNA double strand breaks. These interrelationships can only be observed when the measurements of survival and aberration yield, or survival and mutation frequency, or survival and double strand breaks are made in the same experiments.

We hope that you are able to follow the pathway from the molecular lesion, ie. the DNA double strand break, to the three cellular effects. We also hope that you appreciate the different effectiveness of densely ionising radiation, like fast neutrons, compared with sparsely ionising radiation, like gamma rays. You now know that this is associated with a different efficiency for inducing 'primary' double strand breaks (A value). And we hope you recognise that a reduction of dose rate of sparsely ionising radiation leads to a reduction of the effect (β goes to 0). This is because the cell can repair DNA single strand breaks perfectly during protracted exposures.

Now for the health effects!

6.7 Health Effects

At the beginning of this book, three effects of radiation were described:

Short-term effects, such as radiation sickness, that are associated with a substantial radiation exposure and become apparent within a few days of the exposure;

Cancer that is the important late effect caused by radiation and arises several years after an exposure;

Hereditary effects, such as mutations, that can be revealed in future generations.

In the introduction to the previous chapter, it was proposed that the radiation-induced health effects arise from cellular disfunctions. The following two chapters deal with the short-term effects and the induction of cancer in relation to the cellular effects, aberrations, mutations and survival, described in this chapter.

Hereditary mutations were briefly mentioned in section 6.3 as a cellular effect in association with mutations in general.

Figure 6.18, which builds on figure 6.1, demonstrates how the path from the DNA double strand breaks, through the cellular effects, is extended to the health effects.

Short-term effects, such as radiation sickness or anaemia, are associated with substantial cell killing and this association is developed in the following chapter.

The **late effect, radiation-induced cancer,** is associated with mutations and aberrations but also with a role for cell killing. This association is developed in chapter 8.

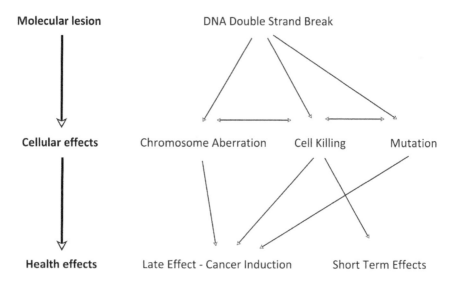

Figure 6.18 *A simple diagram of the pathway from the radiation-induced molecular lesion, ie. DNA double strand breaks, via the three different cellular effects to the short-term health effects and the late health effect which is cancer.*

 And Our Take Home Message is:

Don't forget that the health effects result from cellular disfunctions and they are caused by DNA double strand breaks!

CHAPTER 7

The Short-term Effects of Radiation

7.1 Introduction

The short-term, or acute, effects of radiation, such as radiation sickness, anaemia, organ damage, skin burn and, ultimately, death become apparent within a few days to a few weeks of exposure to substantial doses of radiation. Most of these short-term effects result from a total body exposure to penetrating radiation, such as gamma rays or energetic X-rays, although there are exceptions. Skin burn, for example, could arise from an exposure to low energy X-rays or beta radiation. In radiation therapy to treat cancer, large radiation doses are administered to very localised parts of the body at the tumour site and, in a radiation accident situation, partial shielding could lead to a partial body exposure. Nevertheless, these acute effects of radiation invariably show a relationship with radiation dose which has a quite typical shape and is illustrated in figure 7.1. The dose-effect relationships for these effects, which were investigated in small animals many years ago, exhibit a 'threshold' or range of dose where no effect is observed, followed by a sharp decline over a relatively small, further increase in dose. It is just as if the effect reaches a tipping point of dose after which it falls off a cliff.

These effects almost certainly arise as a consequence of massive cell killing. As was explained earlier, most of the cells in the body have stopped dividing and are busy doing their specific job in their specific organ or tissue. These cells will not divide any more but, in most tissues and organs, there is a slow turnover of cells as some die and are replaced. Each specific organ and tissue has a small pool of stem cells whose task is to replace any dying cells in that organ or tissue and maintain the organ or tissue in its normal state. In some organs and tissues, such as the lining of the stomach, or the blood or the hair, there is a constant replenishment of cells and, consequently, a continuous level of stem cell

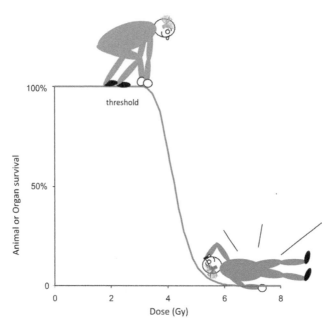

Figure 7.1 *A pictorial representation of a typical dose-effect relationship for animal or organ survival after high doses of acute, penetrating radiation.*

division. An acute exposure to a large dose of penetrating radiation, such as gamma rays, causes a high level of cell killing of both normal and stem cells, and a subsequent surge in stem cell division to replace the dead cells and ensure survival. The explanation proposed here for these short-term effects is based on the conviction that a proportion of the stem cells of each organ or tissue needs to survive for the whole organism to survive. In other words, when too many stem cells are killed by the radiation dose, the organ or tissue replacement will not occur and the organism (the exposed person or animal) will die.

And the Take Home Message is:

The short-term effects such as radiation sickness, anaemia or organism survival resulting from a large exposure to radiation are directly associated with massive stem cell killing.

7.2 Explaining and Quantifying the Effect

How does this massive stem cell killing explain the dose-effect relationship (see figure 7.1) for these effects?

Well, in the threshold range of dose, although radiation is killing cells, including the stem cells, there is still a sufficient number of surviving stem cells so that the damage to the organ or tissue can be repaired to a normally functioning state. Consequently, no effect of, for example, organ failure or animal death, is observed. At a certain level of dose, 'at the edge of the cliff', the number of surviving stem cells capable of repairing the organ or tissue becomes critical and the first signs of the effect become apparent. As the dose increases further, the number of surviving stem cells decreases rapidly and the effect 'falls off the cliff' until all the animals die.

For the more mathematically inclined amongst you, we can quantify this as a function of dose using the single cell survival equation developed in the previous chapter, namely:

$$S = \exp\{-p(AD + BD^2)\}.$$

Consider now multiple cell killing and a short-term effect such as animal survival, designated here as "vitality" (V). An equation for animal vitality can be derived from the single cell survival as:

$$V = 1 - [1 - S]^n = 1 - [1 - (\exp\{-p(AD + BD^2)\})]^n,$$

where (1/n) is the proportion of stem cells which need to survive for the animal to survive.

The word "vitality" has been chosen to indicate the ability of an organ or organism to continue functioning normally. The word will not be found in the radiobiological scientific literature used in this context.

The vitality equation is represented graphically in figure 7.2 together with some actual data on mouse survival. At 100% vitality (simply =

100V), all of the animals survive and this extends for a considerable threshold until the critical 'cliff edge' dose is reached and animals start to die as the dose increases further.

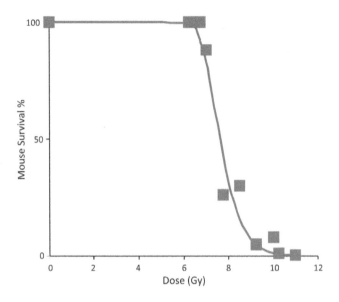

Figure 7.2 *A graphical presentation of some data from the 1960s on mouse survival (vitality) after exposure to total body gamma radiation with a curve drawn to fit the data using the red equation for vitality.*

 And Our Take Home Message is:

Because short-term effects are associated with massive stem cell killing, it is possible to derive a relationship between single cell survival and vitality (animal or organ survival) which can be quantified.

7.3 Single Cell Survival and Vitality

It is informative to overdraw the vitality graph with the single cell survival graph which means that it is necessary to turn to a logarithmic scale on the vertical axis. This combination is presented in figure 7.3 for (n) equal to 1000 (chosen for convenience), which means that one-thousandth of the number of stem cells in the relevant organ or tissue must survive if the animal is to survive.

Here it can be seen that the single cell survival curve starts well above the vitality curve and that, as the dose increases along the 'threshold' with no effect on vitality, the cell survival curve decreases considerably. For instance, figure 7.3 shows that, at a dose of 2 Gy, although vitality is still 100% in the threshold region, the single cell survival curve is down from 1000 to 100 indicating that 90% of the cells have been killed. In other words, although there is no observable effect on vitality, substantial cell killing occurs in the animal. At the 'cliff edge' dose for vitality, only one-thousandth of the cells survive and the two curves get very close to each other down the 'cliff'.

The important message is that, although no effect is observable on vitality in the threshold dose region, large amounts of radiation damage are caused in the form of substantial cell killing.

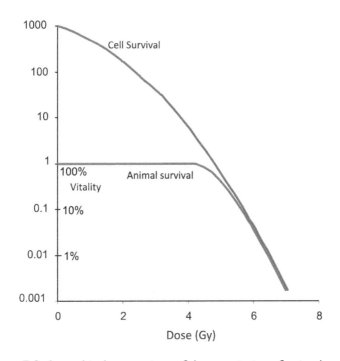

Figure 7.3 A graphical comparison of the association of animal or organ survival, following the red equation, and the cell survival of the stem cells, following the magenta equation. The red curve here is closely similar to that shown in figure 7.2 but drawn on a vertical logarithmic scale.

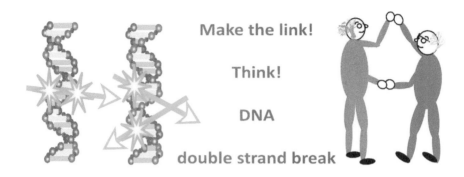

Make the link!

Think!

DNA

double strand break

7.4 Vitality after Exposure to Densely Ionising Radiation

The only penetrating type of densely ionising radiation from an external source which is capable of causing a total body exposure is fast neutrons. Alpha particles cannot penetrate the skin but, if an alpha particle emitter is ingested and spreads throughout the tissues of the body, a comparable total body exposure to densely ionising radiation is possible. (Remember Litvinenko!)

By combining what has been learnt about the effects of different types of radiation on cell killing with the overdrawing of the cell survival curve and the vitality curve, insight can be gained into how the effect of densely ionising radiation will alter the vitality curve.

In chapter 6, it was shown in the discussion of cellular effects that densely ionising radiation increases the value (A) and that the single cell survival curve is steeper than that for sparsely ionising radiation. This is reflected in figure 7.4 where the single cell survival curve for densely ionising radiation (in turquoise) is much steeper than that for sparsely ionising radiation (in magenta) and this steeper curve leads to a shortening of the vitality threshold (in green) so that the 'cliff edge' occurs at a lower dose.

To illustrate this more clearly, in figure 7.5, the vitality curves from figure 7.4 are drawn in the more conventional way and figure 7.6 presents some real data for comparison.

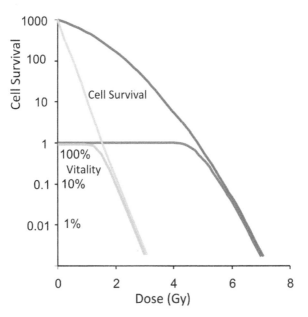

Figure 7.4 *A graphical representation of the effect of densely ionising radiation on vitality (in green) compared with the effect of sparsely ionising radiation (in red). The relevant single cell survival curves (in turquoise and magenta) are also drawn for comparison with figure 7.3 and to show that vitality reflects single cell survival. It is assumed that organ survival (vitality) starts to decrease when only one-thousandth of the stem cell population survives.*

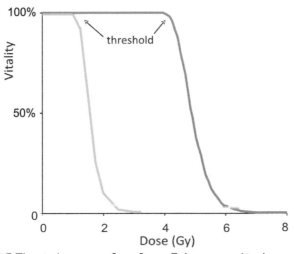

Figure 7.5 *The vitality curves from figure 7.4 presented in the conventional way. The curve for densely ionising radiation (in green) has a shortened threshold compared with the curve for sparsely ionising radiation (in red).*

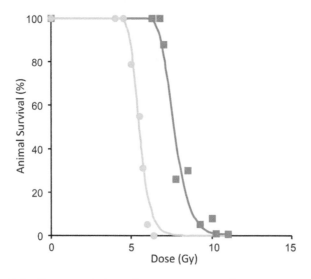

Figure 7.6 *Some real data for mouse survival, equivalent to vitality, after fast neutron exposure compared with the data for sparsely ionising radiation shown in figure 7.2*

Prof Dee and Dr Hay's Take Home Message is:

Knowing that the cellular response to densely ionising radiation exhibits a larger value of (A) with a steeper survival curve, allows us to predict a shorter threshold in vitality. Total body exposure to densely ionising radiation (fast neutrons) causes animal or organ killing at lower doses.

7.5 The Effect of Extending the Time of Exposure on Vitality

Using the knowledge acquired in chapter 6 of how single cell survival is influenced by protracting the dose over a few days, insight can be gained into how this will affect vitality. In chapter 6, it was shown that protracting the dose reduces its effectiveness because the value of (B) for the induction of 'secondary' double strand breaks goes to zero. This is a consequence of the perfect repair of DNA single strand breaks during exposure and leads to the equation for single cell survival as:

$$S = \exp\{-p(AD)\}.$$

And this leads to the equation for vitality (animal or organ survival) as:

$$V = 1 - [1 - S]^n = 1 - [1 - (\exp\{-p(AD)\})]^n.$$

In figure 7.7, this is illustrated for single cell survival and vitality with n =1000.

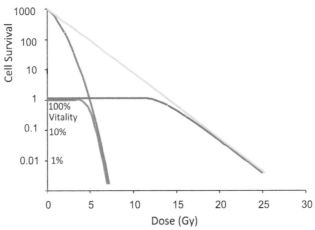

Figure 7.7 *A graphical representation of the effect that protracting the dose of sparsely ionising radiation has on single cell survival (pale blue) and on vitality. The vitality at low dose rate shows an extended threshold and a more gentle 'cliff'. The single cell survival (magenta) and vitality (red) are for an acute exposure and are the same lines as drawn in figures 7.3 and 7.4. (Note the change in scale of the Dose axis.)*

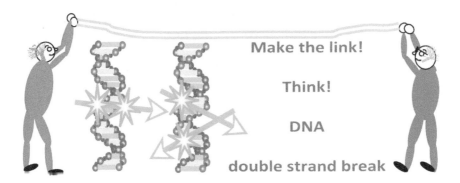

In the case of sparsely ionising radiation, where the single cell survival curve is dominated at higher doses by the quadratic term in dose (BD^2), a substantial effect on vitality can be seen when the exposure is extended over a few days or longer. This is because the number of 'secondary' DNA double strand breaks and, consequently (BD^2), decreases as the exposure time is extended. The threshold increases considerably, the 'cliff edge' moves to a higher dose and the 'cliff' itself is more like a steep slope down.

In figure 7.8, the vitality curves from figure 7.7 are drawn in the more conventional way and figure 7.9 presents some real data for comparison.

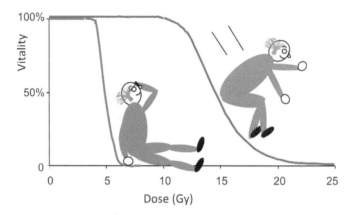

Figure 7.8 *A conventional representation of the effect of reduced dose rate on vitality. A protracted exposure (blue) leads to an extended threshold and a more gentle drop off in vitality. The red line shows vitality after an acute exposure to gamma or X-rays and is the same as the red line shown in figure 7.5.*

The considerable extension of the threshold for low dose rate gamma or X-rays should be reassuring as both the general public and radiation workers are never exposed to such high doses of these radiations. Only in extreme emergency conditions will radiation workers be exposed to high dose rates and even then their exposure dose levels will be very carefully controlled within the threshold to avoid short-term health effects.

In the case of densely ionising radiation, extending the time of exposure makes very little difference to both single cell survival and vitality. This is because both curves are dominated by the linear term in dose (AD) and because this term is independent of the time over which exposure occurs.

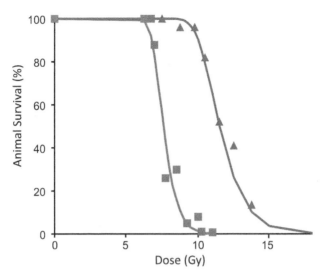

Figure 7.9 *Some real data on animal survival, equivalent to vitality, for low dose rate exposure of mice to sparsely ionising radiation compared with the data for an acute exposure from figure 7.2*

 And Our Take Home Message is:

Once again our knowledge of the cellular response to a reduced dose rate exposure allows us to predict that vitality will exhibit a considerably longer threshold and a shallower 'cliff' than it would after an acute exposure.

7.6 Summary

The short-term effects caused by substantial doses of radiation, such as radiation sickness, anaemia or vitality, are directly associated with massive stem cell killing.

These effects usually arise within a few days to a few weeks following exposure.

The dose-effect relationships for these sorts of effects have a long threshold of dose, where no effect is apparent, followed by a steep decline.

A total body dose of 4 to 5 Gy of sparsely ionising radiation accumulated in a short period of time will kill 50% of the exposed population.

The dose-effect relationship for these effects can be related to the single cell survival equation derived in chapter 6 which is a linear-quadratic function of dose.

The influence of radiation type and dose rate on the single cell survival equation is reflected in the influence that radiation type and dose rate have on the short-term effects.

 The Important Messages are:

Densely ionising radiation, which we know increases the value of (A), reduces the vitality threshold and the 'cliff edge' occurs at a lower dose.

Extending the time over which a dose is accumulated for sparsely ionising radiation such as gamma and X-rays, increases considerably the vitality threshold. The 'cliff edge' moves to a higher dose and becomes less of a 'cliff' and more of a 'steep slope down'.

This information is important for the radiation protection of special staff involved, for example, in the clean up of a reactor accident, such as Fukushima or Chernobyl, where some personnel will accumulate doses somewhat larger than is routinely accepted for radiation workers. It can also be important for radiation therapy where cancer victims are treated with high but localised radiation doses, invariably administered in fractions, in order to kill the tumour cells. The aim here is to get as large a dose as possible in the tumour cells while having a much smaller dose in the surrounding healthy tissue.

Under normal conditions, the general public will never be exposed to radiation dose levels which might cause short-term effects. Only in extreme accident conditions might exposures to such large doses be accumulated and, even then, it is probable that only radiation workers will be involved.

It should always be borne in mind that, although no effect of radiation exposure on vitality is apparent within the long dose threshold, that is before the effect 'falls off the cliff', a substantial amount of cell killing will still take place.

CHAPTER 8

Radiation-Induced Cancer

8.1 Introduction

Radiation-induced cancer is the most important 'late' effect of radiation exposure. In contrast to the short-term effects, it is called a late effect because it develops several years after exposure. The severity of the cancer is not related to the dose of radiation whereas the likelihood of getting a cancer is dependent on the dose and increases as the dose gets bigger. It is the effect of radiation which is the most invidious and the most feared and it is this effect which provides the basis for the estimates of radiation risk. International recommendations on limits of radiation exposure for both people who work with radiation and the general population are derived from the assessments of the risks for cancer found in groups of people, for example the atomic bomb survivors, who have been exposed in the past.

The development of cancer as a consequence of radiation exposure first became noticed in the early 20th century when several of the pioneering scientists working with radiation and radioactivity eventually suffered from the disease. At this time, radiation was considered beneficial and exposures were not limited. Another group who suffered from the incautious use of radioactivity in the early days were the luminous instrument-dial painters who 'pointed' the brush between their lips and ingested substantial amounts of radium from the luminous paint. Many of the dial painters, mainly young women, developed bone cancers in the head and neck. However, it was not until some 5 years after the bombing of Hiroshima and Nagasaki in 1945, that the potential for radiation to induce cancer became widely acknowledged. In the early 1950s, leukaemia was found to be occurring in the atomic bomb survivors at unanticipated levels and, as a consequence, Japan and the USA set up a special research programme to study the health effects arising in the survivors. That programme still runs today and has revealed that virtually all naturally occurring forms of cancer can also be induced by radiation.

The association of chromosomal damage with cancer was first proposed in the early 1900s and stimulated the idea that a somatic mutation could be an important step in the development of the disease. Over the years, several cancers were found to be linked to typical chromosomal changes which strengthened the concept. Nowadays, as a result of recent developments in molecular biology, DNA analysis of different cancers has revealed that mutations in somatic cells are very commonly associated with cancer. Specific types of mutation are linked with specific cancers. For example, two specific mutations are associated with breast cancer in women. Although these mutations account for only a small proportion of all breast cancers, the women who carry them are at an increased risk of getting breast cancer. Interestingly, one of these mutations is associated with poor repair of DNA double strand breaks. Consequently, the approach adopted here to describe radiation-induced cancer is to start from the equation derived in chapter 6 for radiation-induced mutations.

Dr Hay and Prof Dee's Take Home Message is:

Radiation can induce all naturally occurring cancers. Cancer is strongly associated with chromosome aberrations and mutations.

8.2 Quantifying the Effect

The full equation used to describe mutation frequency per surviving cell (M) is:

$$M = 1 - \exp\{-q(N)\} = 1 - \exp\{-q(AD + BD^2)\}$$

and figure 6.11 revealed that this equation curves upwards at low doses but eventually turns flat to approach the value of 1 at high doses. This equation describes the mutation frequency measured in cells which have survived the radiation exposure.

However, in the case of cancer induction, it is the mutations per irradiated cell that have to be calculated. The mutated cell has to survive the radiation to be able to express the cancer mutation. And this means that the magenta equation above for mutation frequency per surviving cell has to be multiplied by the chance that the cell survives (S) with the result that the cancer induction (CI) is:

$$CI = M^*S = [1 - \exp\{-q(AD + BD^2)\}]^* \exp\{-p(AD + BD^2)\}.$$
(* means multiplied by)

This equation is not as complicated as it may seem. It simply consists of two separate terms, mutation induction and cell survival. The graphical representation of this equation is shown in red in figure 8.1.

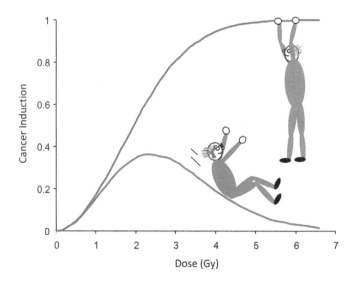

Figure 8.1 *A graphical representation of the cancer induction curve (in red) described by the red equation compared with the equation for mutations (in magenta) described by the magenta equation. The cancer induction curve is 'pulled down' from the mutations curve because more and more cells that are mutated are also killed at higher doses. If the 'mutated to cancer' cell does not survive, it cannot express the cancer.*

The mutations (magenta line) curve upwards to saturate at a value of 1, while fewer and fewer of the cells survive at higher doses. They pull the cancer induction graph (red line) downwards. So, although the red equation curves upwards at low doses, it eventually turns over as cell killing starts to dominate and, at higher doses, the cancer induction becomes very small. Figure 8.2 presents some experimental data, fitted with the cancer induction (CI) equation, for radiation-induced leukaemia in mice.

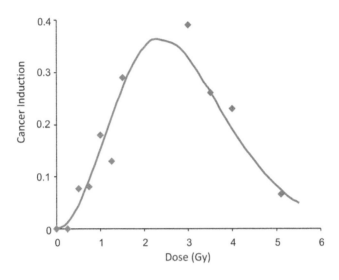

Figure 8.2 *Some data (red diamonds) for leukaemia induction in mice following gamma radiation, with the red equation for cancer induction drawn through the data. The maximum cancer induction of 0.37 means that, at the peak, 37% of the animals exposed to 2.5 Gy would get the cancer.*

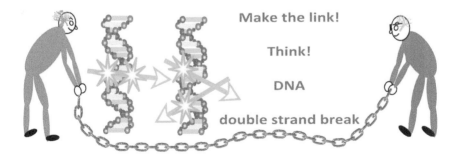

8.3 Radiation-induced Cancer comes from a Somatic Mutation

The cancer induction (CI) equation has an interesting mathematical feature which permits the derivation of strong experimental evidence in support of the idea that radiation-induced cancer arises from a somatic mutation. This feature is that the peak value of the cancer induction (CI) equation remains the same and is independent of the values of (*A*) and (*B*). So, if experiments for cancer induction in animals can be found where the peak height remains constant under different radiation exposure conditions, then those data provide evidence for the association of cancer induction with radiation-induced somatic mutations.

In figure 8.3, some experimental data is presented which supports this association. The actual peak value depends on the animal cancer system being studied but, if the peak value remains constant within an experimental system, then the evidence is convincing.

And the Take Home Message is:

The same peak height in animal data, independent of the radiation conditions, is very strong evidence for the association of radiation-induced cancer with mutation! You will see a couple of examples below.

The more mathematical amongst you can prove this for yourselves by differentiating the CI equation with respect to dose and equating the differential with zero. This should reveal that the peak height, which is where the differential is equal to zero, is independent of (*A*), (*B*) and (D) and only dependent on the values of (p) and (q) and is:

$$CI_{peak} = [1 - p/(p+q)]^{*}[p/(p+q)]^{p/q}.$$

The constant peak height is a consequence of the interrelationship between mutation induction and cell survival and goes back to the proposal that the same type of molecular lesion, the DNA double strand break, is responsible for the different cellular effects.

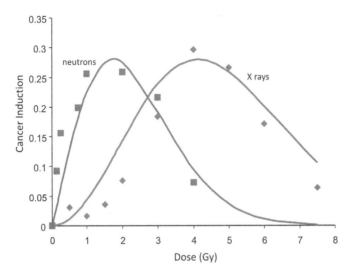

Figure 8.3 *Some data on the induction of lung cancer in rats induced by X-rays (red) and neutrons (magenta). The cancer induction equation is drawn through both sets of data and illustrates the same peak height in cancer induction, independent of whether the radiation was X-rays or neutrons. These data support the association of radiation-induced cancer with mutation. In this case, some 28% of the animals would get lung cancer at the peak.*

8.4 Cancer Induction after Densely Ionising Radiation

You have seen that densely ionising radiation increases the value of (*A*) and that the dose-effect relationships become less curved, more linear and move to lower doses. When this is introducd into the equation for cancer induction, the peaked curve becomes more 'pointy' and the peak moves to lower doses. However, the peak height remains the same as for sparsely ionising radiation. This is represented graphically in figure 8.4 which also presents some data for the induction of cancer in animals.

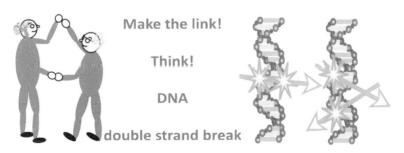

Make the link!

Think!

DNA

double strand break

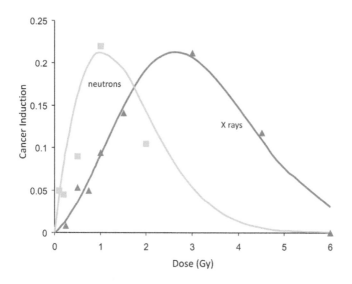

Figure 8.4 *Some data for the induction of leukaemia in mice after exposure to either X-rays (red triangles) or neutrons (green squares) with the cancer induction equation drawn through both sets of data. Note that the neutrons are more effective at low doses and that although the peaks have the same height, the neutron peak occurs at a lower dose than that for X-rays.*

The important conclusion from these graphs is that low doses of densely ionising radiation will be more efficient at inducing cancer than low doses of sparsely ionising radiation. The importance of this conclusion will become apparent when radiation protection issues are discussed in the next chapter.

 And Our Take Home Message is:

Once more, the increased effectiveness of densely ionising radiation (neutrons) that we found in the cellular effects is revealed in the cancer induction data. But, of course, if cancer arises from mutation, this is exactly what we expect.....make the link – think – DNA double strand breaks!

8.5 The Effect of Extending the Time of Exposure on Cancer Induction

In the cellular effects described in chapter 6, it was shown that extending the time of exposure leads to a decrease in the value of (B) until, at exposure times of more than a few hours or days, the value of (B) becomes zero. Especially in the case of sparsely ionising radiation, this decreases the curvature of the dose-effect relationship until it becomes linear.

In figure 8.5, the cancer induction curve for sparsely ionising radiation, such as gamma rays and X-rays, is drawn. As the exposure time increases, the value of (B) decreases, the graph becomes less curved and the peak value is pushed out to higher doses. However, the peak value will always remain the same. When the value of (B) becomes zero, the equation for cancer induction becomes:

$$CI = [1 - \exp\{(-q\mathcal{A}D)\}]^* \exp\{(-p\mathcal{A}D)\}.$$

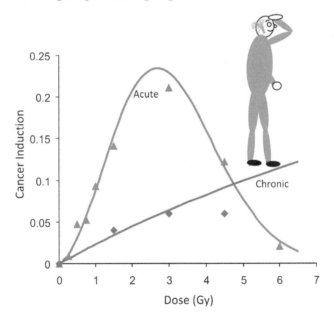

Figure 8.5 *The effect of reducing the exposure dose rate of sparsely ionising radiation (X-rays) on cancer induction. The red triangles and line are for an acute exposure. The blue diamonds and line are for a chronic exposure to X-rays and illustrate the reduced cancer induction of the low dose rate exposure.*

111

The graph of cancer induction from low dose rate, sparsely ionising radiation, becomes linear in the lower dose region and the peak value of cancer induction moves out to very high doses.

The important conclusion from this graph is that the chance for cancer induction from gamma rays and X-rays at low dose rate increases in proportion with increasing dose from zero dose upwards. Even though the slope of the graph is much less than for densely ionising radiation, the induction of cancer by radiation does not show any threshold at all. This is in contrast with the short-term effects that were considered in chapter 7.

Prof Dee and Dr Hay's Take Home Message is:

This result is of crucial importance for the assessment of radiation risks because we are all exposed to very small doses of background radiation throughout our lives.

In the case of densely ionising radiation, you know that the value of (*B*) plays a much smaller role because of the dominance of the larger (*A*) value. This means that extending the time of exposure to densely ionising radiation has a much smaller effect on the peaked curve of cancer induction. This can be seen in figure 8.6.

Once more it is important to note that for low doses of short-term, acute exposures or long-term, protracted exposures, the dose-effect relationship for cancer induction is defined by the value of (*A*). At higher doses for long-term, protracted exposures the dose-effect relationship is also defined by the value of (*A*). This is crucial for the development of radiation protection philosophy and implies that it is the value of (*A*), for the induction of 'primary' DNA double strand breaks, that governs the risks of ionising radiations.

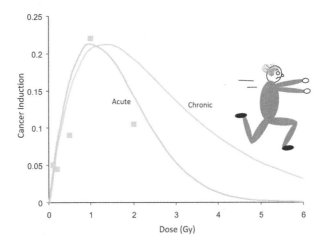

Figure 8.6 *The effect of reducing exposure dose rate of densely ionising radiation (neutrons) on cancer induction. The green squares and line are for an acute exposure and the blue curve is what would be expected if the exposure dose rate was reduced. There is very little change in effect especially at low doses (the rising portions of both lines).*

8.6 Summary

The same peak height of cancers in animals induced under different radiation conditions implies that radiation-induced cancer arises from a somatic mutation.

The full mutation frequency equation, derived for cellular mutations, multiplied by the equation for cell survival, provides an equation which can be fitted to radiation-induced cancers in animals. The graph of the equation starts at low doses with a linear-quadratic upwards curvature but passes through a peak and decreases at higher doses as a result of cell killing.

Exposure to densely ionising radiation makes the equation more linear and pointy and moves the peak to lower doses. Extending the time of exposure to densely ionising radiation (fast neutrons, alpha particles) does not alter the shape of the graph very much.

Extending the time of exposure to sparsely ionising radiation (gamma rays, X-rays) makes the graph more linear at lower doses and pushes the peak to much higher doses, thus considerably reducing the effect of radiation on cancer induction at lower doses.

And Our Take Home Message is:

The major conclusion for us is that at low doses and low dose rates, the induction of cancer by sparsely ionising radiation is linearly proportional with dose from zero dose up. Therefore, there is no threshold dose below which the chance for cancer induction from radiation does not occur.

This conclusion is central to the philosphy that lies behind the discipline of radiation protection which is briefly discussed in the next chapter.

CHAPTER 9

Radiation Protection

9.1 Introduction

Many of you will be surprised to learn that the protection of man from radiation has been very comprehensively developed for some eighty years by an international body of concerned scientists. The International Commission on Radiological Protection (ICRP) is a completely independent organisation that has, over the years, developed recommendations for the protection of the general public and workers in the radiation industry from the risks that radiation exposure can cause. These recommendations are based on a thoroughly grounded philosophy incorporating the principle that exposures should always be "as low as readily achievable" (ALARA) and are accepted and implemented everywhere in the world. The ICRP are continually reviewing and updating their reports on the various aspects of radiological protection and regularly issue revised recommendations.

And the Take Home Message is:

Radiation Protection has been around a long time and is based on internationally recognised recommendations to limit the exposure of us all.

9.2 ICRP and the Linear No-Threshold Concept

The ICRP considers that the major risk from low doses of radiation is the induction of cancer. Its philosophy on radiological protection is based on the idea that the dose-effect relationship for cancer is proportional with radiation dose from zero dose up. This concept has been given the name of 'linear no-threshold' (LNT).

Several years ago, the ICRP decided that the data on leukaemia in atomic bomb survivors indicated that the dose-effect relationship was linear with dose, even though this meant they ignored the reduced incidence data at higher doses. The slope of this linear dose-effect relationship was assumed to give a value for the high dose-rate risk for leukaemia induction from sparsely ionising radiation. At the same time, the ICRP recognised that radiobiological data implied a reduction in the induced effect when the exposure was protracted and so they introduced a dose and dose-rate effectiveness factor (DDREF) of 2.

Consequently, the ICRP divided the slope of the linear dose-effect relationship giving the high dose-rate risk for leukaemia by the DDREF of 2 to define the risk for leukaemia induction. This risk was considered valid for all sparsely ionising radiations at small doses but also at larger doses if accumulated over an extended period of time (i.e. at low dose rate). This procedure is presented graphically in figure 9.1 which illustrates the ICRP derivation of radiation risk for chronic (low dose-rate) exposures to sparsely ionising radiation. The figure shows some data for leukaemia incidence in atomic bomb survivors (magenta diamonds) with a straight line through the rising data (magenta line) representing the ICRP interpretation of the data. The turquoise straight line has exactly half the slope of the magenta line and is taken as an indication of the low dose, low dose-rate risk from sparsely ionising radiation. It is worth noting that the atomic bomb survivors were exposed to a very acute dose of energetic gamma rays.

The ICRP have used the risk for leukaemia induction at low doses and low dose rates to develop an overall risk for the induction of all cancers at low doses and low dose rates of 4% per Sv. The sievert (Sv), you will recall, is the unit of dose equivalent used in radiation protection to compare the risks of all types of radiation (see chapter 3). All the recommendations issued by the ICRP for limiting worker and population exposures are based on this value of risk.

The ICRP also recognised that densely ionising radiations were considerably more efficient at inducing damaging effects than sparsely ionising radiations. They defined 'radiation weighting factors' which

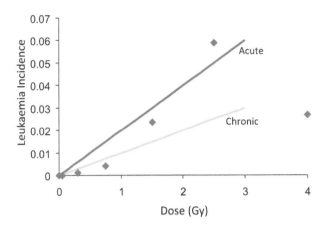

Figure 9.1 *A graphical representation of the way that the ICRP has derived the radiation risk for chronic exposure to sparsely ionising radiation from atomic bomb survivor data.*

could be applied to the doses measured in gray (Gy) to convert to the dose equivalent of exposure in sievert (Sv). As a result, the same value of risk could be applied to all the different types of radiation. In doing this, the ICRP ascribed the radiation weighting factor of 1 to all sparsely ionising radiations (gamma rays, X-rays and beta rays), a value of 10 for fast neutrons and protons and 20 for alpha particles and other densely ionising radiations found around particle accelerators.

Although the ICRP philosophy is widely respected and implemented, there are some radiation scientists who do not accept the linear no-threshold concept and think that there is a threshold of radiation dose below which cancer is not induced. These scientists, therefore, do not accept the idea that low doses of radiation have any damaging health effects.

9.3 The Use of the Linear No-Threshold Concept Here

In the previous chapter, it was concluded that at low dose rates of sparsely ionising radiation the risk for radiation-induced cancer was linear with dose from zero dose up. Consequently, the linear no-threshold concept of radiation-induced cancer is whole-heartedly endorsed here. However, the comprehensive explanation of radiation effects developed in earlier chapters leads to conclusions about low dose risk which differ considerably from the ICRP philosophy and several comments are required.

In the first place, the linear-quadratic equation for cancer incidence (see chapter 8):

$$CI = M^*S = [1 - \exp\{-q(AD + BD^2)\}]^*\exp\{-p(AD + BD^2)\}$$

should be used to analyse all the data on the induction of leukaemia in atomic bomb survivors. This includes the decreased induction of leukaemia data found at higher doses which is ignored by the ICRP. This is illustrated in figure 9.2. Then the same equation, but with the value of (B) set to zero, would be used to derive the dose-effect relationship for protracted, or low dose-rate exposures, namely:

$$CI = [1 - \exp\{(-qAD)\}]^*\exp\{(-pAD)\}.$$

This is also shown in figure 9.2.

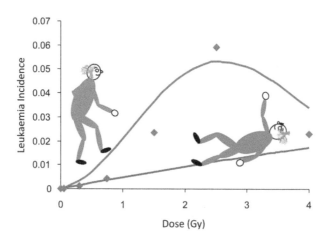

Figure 9.2 *A graphical representation of the proposed interpretation of atomic bomb survivor data and derivation of the low dose, low dose-rate risk of sparsely ionising radiation. The red diamonds are exactly the same data as shown in figure 9.1 in magenta. The red line is drawn using the red equation to fit all the data and the blue line is drawn using the blue equation when the value of (B) is zero.*

The straight line (blue) interpretation of the atomic bomb survivor data used here to derive the low dose, low dose-rate risk of sparsely ionising radiation, defined by the value (qA), provides a direct link between the risk and the induction of 'primary' DNA double strand breaks. In previous chapters, the influence of radiation type on the induction of 'primary' DNA double strand breaks and consequently, on the value of (A), has been repeatedly demonstrated (see chapter 5 and figure 5.8).

This means that the low dose, low dose-rate risk of radiation will be strongly dependent on the type of radiation. Alpha particle exposure and protons from fast neutron exposure will have a higher level of risk compared to gamma rays and X-rays.

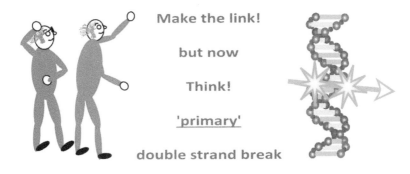

Make the link!

but now

Think!

'primary'

double strand break

Dr Hay and Prof Dee's Take Home Message is:

We think we have a better interpretation than the ICRP as we can trace it all back to the molecular lesion, DNA double strand breaks.

A comparison of the ICRP interpretation of the atomic bomb survivor data and the interpretation proposed here is shown graphically in figure 9.3 which reveals that the rising portion of the linear-quadratic equation (a forward leaning, flattened S shape) can be approximated quite closely by a straight line. This explains why the ICRP chose a straight-line fit to the rising leukaemia data. Figure 9.3 also reveals that the straight line, low dose and low dose-rate risk (blue line) derived here and defined by the value of (qA) is different from the low dose, low dose-rate risk (turquoise line) derived by the ICRP.

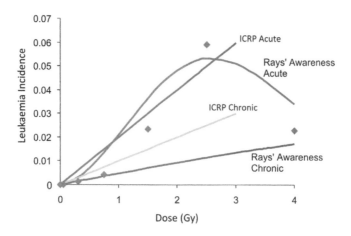

Figure 9.3 *A comparison of the two different Linear No-Threshold (LNT) interpretations of atomic bomb survivor data presented in figures 9.1 and 9.2.*

However, because the fitting of the linear-quadratic equation to the data is dominated by the quadratic part of the equation and the value of (*B*), the value of (q*A*) derived from the fitting does have large errors. This means that it will always be very difficult to derive an accurate value for the low dose, low dose-rate radiation risk from atomic bomb data using the linear-quadratic equation.

In addition, it needs to be remembered that the atomic bomb survivors were exposed to high energy gamma rays which would be expected to be less efficient at inducing 'primary' DNA double strand breaks than the mix of sparsely ionising radiation to which radiation workers and the general population are exposed.

So, although the value for low dose, low dose-rate risk derived from atomic bomb survivor data here is lower than that derived by the ICRP, the ICRP interpretation might well provide a useful estimate of risk for sparsely ionising radiation in general.

Thus, in spite of the serious doubts about the scientific merit of the way that the ICRP have arrived at their choice of risk, the ICRP estimate of risk is acceptable. Moreover, it is important to recognise that the

ICRP philosophy and recommendations have created an internationally accepted and implemented, comprehensive set of procedures for the control of all exposures to workers in the radiation industry and to the general population.

Prof Dee and Dr Hay's Take Home Message is:

Although we think our interpretation is better, we have to say that the ICRP has "guess-timated" a useful value for low dose radiation risk but some further considerations are needed.

With respect to the effectiveness of different types of radiation, the approach taken here leads to the conclusion that not all types of sparsely ionising radiations will have the same effectiveness in producing 'primary' DNA double strand breaks. This differs from the ICRP's choice of ascribing the same effectiveness to all sparsely ionising radiations.

The association of the DNA double strand break with the induction of mutations and, ultimately, cancer leads to the expectation that the proportion of dose deposited in the form of 'soft or low energy electrons', which are effective 'primary' break inducers, will determine the effectiveness of the sparsely ionising radiation. Energetic gamma rays create energetic electrons which are not effective 'primary' break inducers. Only when these electrons slow down, will they become effective. So, only a small proportion of gamma ray dose is effective in inducing 'primary' double strand breaks. In other words, gamma rays "waste" a fair proportion of dose. Lower energy X-rays (250kVp) create lower energy electrons, are relatively more effective and "waste" a lower proportion of dose. Soft X-rays (90kVp) and low energy beta particles "waste" very little dose. This is illustrated in figure 9.4 and recalls figure 5.8.

On this basis, it can be expected that energetic gamma rays will be less biologically effective (smaller A value) than normal diagnostic X-rays (250kVp) which, in turn, will be less biologically effective than 'soft X-rays' (90kVp), often used in mammography, and low energy beta

121

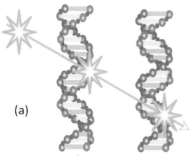

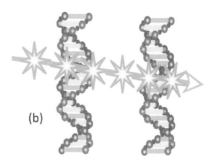

(a)

(b)

Not effective inducers of 'primary'
DNA double strand breaks

More effective inducers of 'primary'
DNA double strand breaks

Figure 9.4 (a) *Energetic gamma rays and X-rays 'waste' a larger proportion of dose, producing ineffective inducers of 'primary' DNA double stand breaks whilst (b) 'softer', lower energy gamma rays and X-rays utilise a larger proportion of dose, producing more effective inducers of 'primary' DNA double strand breaks.*

radiation from, for example, tritium. There are experimental data on the cellular effects of sparsely ionising radiations which support this reasoning and indicate that the value of (*A*) can vary by a factor of three or more from gamma rays to soft X-rays.

Dr Hay and Prof Dee's Take Home Message is:

In contrast to the ICRP, we are rather sure that the effectiveness of all sparsely ionising radiations is not the same. The ICRP need to revise their viewpoint because the general public, as well as radiation workers, will probably be exposed to the more effective sparsely ionising radiations like soft X-rays and tritium beta particles.

The more densely ionising radiations such as fast neutrons, protons and alpha particles will, of course, be much more effective than the sparsely ionising radiations. Whether the values would be as high as the values of 10 and 20, used by the ICRP, is not clear. However, within the aims of a conservative philosophy, the use of these values of 10 and 20 for radiological protection purposes is acceptable.

9.4 Our Exposure to Radiation

You know that everyone is exposed to some background radiation that comes from the radioactivity in the environment and the cosmic radiation from outer space. You also know that the level of exposure to this background radiation varies from place to place but is essentially from sparsely ionising radiations and cannot be avoided. Background exposure is normally around 2.5 thousandths of a sievert (2.5mSv) per year which is small.

However, people living in areas with large deposits of granite which has traces of uranium in it can be exposed to densely ionising background radiation. The uranium-238 decay chain (see figure 2.8) has several alpha particle emitting radionuclides in it, one of which is the gas, radon-222. Although alpha particle emitters do not form an external radiation hazard, they are very effective biologically when they are ingested into the body. Radon gas diffuses from cracks in the granite into the air and decays and the immediate decay products attach to fine dust particles that can be inhaled into the lungs. The radon decay products are short-lived alpha particle emitters (see also figure 2.8) and can thus expose lung tissue to the biologically effective alpha particles. This is not a problem outdoors but can become a problem when radon accumulates in houses built on granite. Considerable attention has been given to reducing the build-up of radon gas in such homes to ensure that the exposure to this gas is kept as low as readily achievable for the occupiers. Radon is also highly soluble in water and the radioactive "daughters" of radon can accumulate in drinking water sources in regions with large granite deposits. Alpha particle emitting radioactivity can be ingested, via the drinking water, to form an internal radiation source.

Workers in the radiation industry, which include not only workers in the nuclear industry but also uranium miners as well as radiographers and radiologists working in hospitals, can be exposed to a variety of different ionising radiations. However, their exposures are very closely and continually measured and their monthly and annual exposures are strictly limited.

No one can escape some low level radiation exposure but this will never cause short-term health effects such as radiation sickness or skin burns. The cells of the body can repair a lot of radiation damage but it should be understood that each increase in exposure brings with it a small increase in the induction of 'primary' DNA double strand breaks. Consequently, there is a small chance of an increase in the occurrence of cancer. The ICRP recommendations are designed to keep this chance to a strict minimum.

 And the Take Home Message is:

Background exposure causes no short-term effects but each exposure increases the chance for cancer, even though this is a very small risk. An exposure of 0.1 Sv (40 years of background exposure) is estimated to give a cancer risk of about 0.5% which should be compared with a natural lifetime cancer risk of about 40%.

The one area of radiation use that does not fall under the umbrella of the ICRP is in medicine. Under normal circumstances, the exposures to diagnostic X-rays, for broken bones or mammography, will not be more than a few thousandths of a sievert (mSv). Computed tomography (CT) scans give a larger exposure but these are not normally in excess of 20mSv. Exceptionally, some special diagnostic procedures can lead to skin burns and this implies considerable cell killing and larger doses. Those undergoing diagnostic examinations are advised not to have too many, too often and to avoid repeated exposures required when records are lost!

Much larger doses of radiation are used in medicine in the therapeutic treatment of tumours. Normally, doses of around 2 gray (2Gy) are administered locally to the tumour in a series of daily fractions up to total doses of 60Gy. The aim is, of course, to get as much dose into the tumour to kill all the tumour cells with a limited exposure to the surrounding healthy tissue. In spite of a variety of special techniques to keep the exposure of the healthy tissue to a minimum, it is impossible not to cause some healthy cell killing and this may lead to transient short-term effects which can be unpleasant but are not usually life-threatening. These medical treatments are considered to be essential for the health of the patient and therefore are not dealt with by the ICRP.

Exposure to radiation levels capable of causing the deleterious short-term health effects will only occur in an absolute emergency or an atomic war. Even in an emergency, it is likely that exposures can be controlled such that the general population will be spared the high acute doses which lead to radiation sickness. The emergency radiation workers will be controlled to avoid high acute doses and only exposed in protracted fractions to decrease the chance of short-term health effects. This was the case at Chernobyl (1986) and at Fukushima (2011) where the highest dose incurred by an emergency worker was below 0.7 Sv. The most important exposure at Chernobyl was that of young children to radioactive iodine, solely because the people living around the reactor were not informed of the accident in time. At Fukushima, stable non-radioactive iodine was swiftly issued to those living close to the reactors to block their thyroids and avoid the uptake of any released radioactive iodine. The thyroid cancers seen in the children living around Chernobyl a few years after the accident should not occur in the population around Fukushima.

Dr Hay and Prof Dee's Take Home Message is:

The hazards of radiation exposure are well recognised and exposure is limited wherever possible. Now that we understand what is happening, if we treat radiation with the respect it deserves, we really do not have to fear it!

CHAPTER 10

UV, Non-Ionising Radiation and Chemicals

10.1 Introduction

In chapter 3, when the different types of ionising radiation were discussed, gamma rays were defined as electro-magnetic radiation, similar in nature to visible light but with a much shorter wavelength and the full spectrum of electro-magnetic radiations was presented in figure 3.3. In figure 10.1, the full spectrum of electro-magnetic radiations is drawn again but, this time, it includes the photon energies and the wavelengths. This figure shows the spectrum running from energetic gamma rays through X-rays and ultraviolet light (UV), into the visible spectrum which goes from blue to red, then infra-red (IR) and then to microwaves and radio waves. The gamma rays have the shortest wavelengths and highest photon energies and the radio waves have the longest wavelengths and lowest photon energies.

The shortest wavelength radiations have the most energetic photons and are very penetrating. Moving to longer wavelengths, the photons become less energetic and in the ultraviolet and visible region they are much less penetrating. Then comes the infra-red and the much longer wavelengths of low energy photons in the microwave and radiowave regions which, nevertheless, are able to pass through and around most matter. As the energy of the photons decreases, they become unable to eject the electrons from the atoms and molecules that make up matter and they become **non-ionising**. In figure 10.1, the photon energies in electron volts have been added for the different regions as have the wavelengths in nanometers and meters. As the wavelength increases, the photon energy decreases. The radiations with a photon energy of more than about 5eV are able to eject electrons from atoms and molecules and are **ionising radiations**. Those with a photon energy of less than about 5eV, that is the ultraviolet regions B and A, visible light, infra-red, microwaves and radio waves are all **non-ionising radiations**. The ultraviolet region C, the most energetic of the ultraviolet regions, can ionise slightly. Solar ultraviolet C radiation is, fortunately for us, absorbed by the atmosphere where it converts oxygen into ozone.

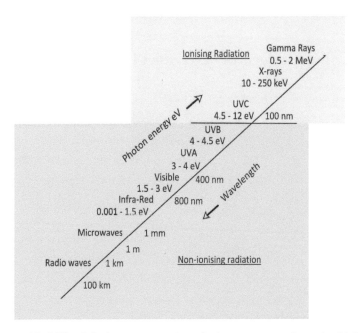

Figure 10.1 *The full electromagnetic radiation spectrum from the highest energy, shortest wavelength gamma rays down to the lowest energy, longest wavelength radio waves.*

By definition, as non-ionising radiations are unable to eject electrons from molecules and break molecular bonds or create free radical species, they are unable to break the DNA molecule. However, ultraviolet light (UVB) is capable of causing single strand deformations in the DNA. These deformations can occur on either strand of the DNA double helix and arise especially where two thymine bases (T) are adjacent to each other along a strand. These deformations are known as '**pyrimidine dimers**'. Each dimer forms a single strand, damaged site on the DNA and since dimers are associated with cell killing and mutations, the effects of UVB deserve special attention.

And the Take Home Message is:

Non-ionising radiation cannot eject electrons from atoms and cannot break chemical bonds. UVB can cause single strand deformations (dimers) in the DNA.

10.2   Cellular Effects of Ultraviolet Light

The major source of ultraviolet radiation is, of course, the sun and the main skin exposure to it is through sunbathing. Sunbathing gives pale skin a "healthy looking" suntan but over-exposure causes sunburn. Some forms of skin cancer are associated with long term exposure to the sun's rays. On the other hand, moderate ongoing exposure to the sun generates vitamin D which has a positive effect on health.

Ultraviolet light (UV) is divided by convention into three regions: UVA, UVB and UVC. UVC has the shortest wavelengths and thus the more energetic photons. UVA, bordering on violet in the visible spectrum, has the longest wavelengths and the lowest energy photons. Fortunately, UVC is absorbed by the atmosphere and does not reach earth and so does not constitute an exposure hazard. UVB and UVA, on the other hand, do pass through the atmosphere and can penetrate the surface layers of the skin. UVB is known to cause deformations in the DNA molecule and is considered to be responsible for effects such as sunburn and skin cancers. UVA, sometimes known as 'black light' and widely used in suntan parlours, is generally thought to be harmless at low exposures but it does cause tanning and might, indirectly, be capable of causing single strand breaks in the DNA.

The model presented in previous chapters on the effects of ionising radiation, invoking the role of DNA double strand breaks, led to investigations into the effects of ultraviolet B. The investigations started from a model originally proposed by an English scientist, James Cleaver and his colleagues, working in America on the repair of UVB induced damage to the DNA. Cleaver's model proposed that a UVB induced deformation in the DNA strand could interfere with DNA replication.

You will remember that the process of replication occurring in the DNA synthesis (S) phase of the cell cycle was described in chapter 4. Replication started at many replicon origins along the DNA and proceeded as the replication forks moved apart bidirectionally until each fork met another fork coming in the opposite direction at the replicon terminus. This is again shown schematically in figure 10.2.

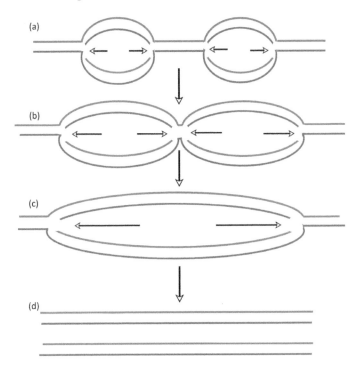

Figure 10.2 *The process of DNA replication in four steps: (a) initiation of many replication 'eyelets' moving towards each other; (b) two replication 'eyelets' reach each other; (c) the 'eyelets' resolve; (d) the stretch of DNA is replicated in a perfect copy. Do not forget that each of the two new double helices carries one old strand from the original helix.*

Cleaver and his colleagues proposed that the progress of the replication fork could be blocked if it encountered a UVB induced deformation (dimer) on the DNA. They suggested that this temporary block would be relieved by the replication fork coming in the other direction, if it continued past the normal replicon terminus. The concepts of Cleaver and his colleagues are presented in a schematic form in figure 10.3.

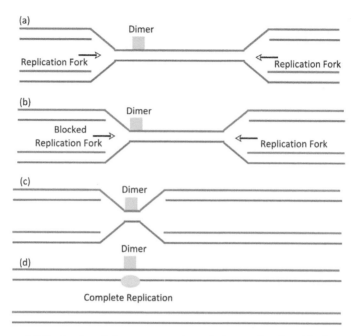

Figure 10.3 *A pictorial representation of the replication block caused by a dimer on one DNA strand and its resolution: (a) replication forks approaching each other; (b) the left hand fork is blocked by the dimer; (c) both replication forks reach the dimer but (d) the right hand fork can pass the dimer and complete the replication process.*

Most importantly, Cleaver and his colleagues proposed that if both replication forks approaching each other were blocked by two UVB induced dimers, one each on opposite DNA strands, a long-lived gap of unreplicated DNA could be a potentially lethal lesion for a cell (see figure 10.4).

And Our Take Home Message is:

Two independently induced dimers, one on each strand of the DNA double helix, can cause a potentially lethal lesion when the replication block is recognised at the time of DNA synthesis (replication).

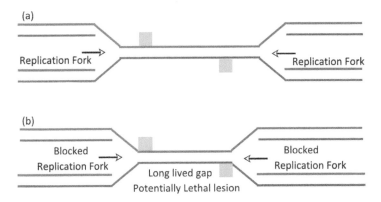

Figure 10.4 *A pictorial representation of the block to replication caused by a pair of dimers, one on each strand of the DNA helix. Cleaver and his colleagues proposed that the long-lived gap might be a potentially lethal lesion.*

10.3 Quantifying the Effects of UV

Using the concepts of Cleaver and his colleagues, a quantitative expression for UV cellular effects can be derived on the basis of the following:

(a) one photon of UV light can cause a single strand deformation, mainly a dimer, in the DNA molecules in the nucleus of a cell.

(b) The single stranded dimers can normally be perfectly repaired in time.

(c) The occurrence of two dimers, one on each strand of the DNA, can eventually form a crucial lesion which has a certain probability of causing cell death or mutation.

(d) The two dimers are only recognised as a crucial lesion at the moment of DNA replication.

The reasoning continues in a way which is comparable to the quantification of DNA double strand breaks and cell killing presented in chapters 5 and 6, although it must be stressed that the UV induced damages in the DNA are not strand breaks but deformations.

If the exposure to UV is defined as (X) and (E_1) is the efficiency per unit exposure for the creation of dimers in one strand of the cellular DNA, then the number of dimers (P_1) in that strand is (E_1) multiplied by the exposure (X), that is:

$$P_1 = E_1 X$$

and the number of dimers (P_2) in the opposite DNA strand is:

$$P_2 = E_2 X.$$

(E_1) and (E_2) will be very similar and might be equal in value.

If a fraction (f) of these dimers is recognised as paired-dimer lesions blocking the replication forks at the moment of DNA replication, then the number of crucial paired-dimer lesions (P) is equal to the number of dimers in strand 1 (P_1) multiplied by the number of dimers in strand 2 (P_2) multiplied by the fraction (f):

$$P = fP_1 P_2 = fE_1 E_2 X^2 \text{ which can be written as: } P = EX^2.$$

This means that the number of crucial, paired-dimer lesions induced by UV exposure is proportional to the square of the UV exposure and this can be represented graphically as shown in figure 10.5(a). A straight line can also be derived from this graph by plotting the number of crucial lesions (P) against the square of the exposure (X^2) as is shown in figure 10.5(b).

If (u) is the chance that a recognised crucial lesion in the DNA causes cell killing (K_{UV}), then:

$$K_{UV} = 1 - \exp(-uP) = 1 - \exp(-uEX^2).$$

This means that cell survival (S_{UV}) after UV exposure is:

$$S_{UV} = 1 - K_{UV} = \exp(-uEX^2).$$

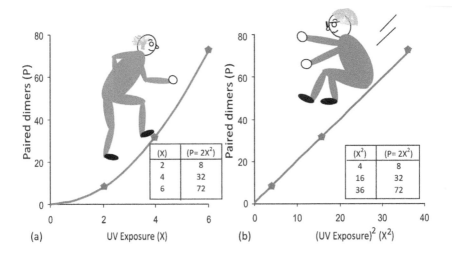

Figure 10.5 (a) A graphical representation of the number of paired-dimer lesions as a function of UV exposure (X) in accordance with the red equation; (b) the same data for paired-dimer lesions drawn in the magenta line as a linear function of the square of the UV exposure (X^2) also in accordance with the red equation. The blue pentagons plot the data in the data boxes.

In figure 10.6(a), this equation is presented graphically together with some experimental data using, as before, a logarithmic scale for survival to unravel the exponential. In figure 10.6(b), the same survival data are presented where the square of exposure is plotted against survival and this reveals the linear relationship predicted by the survival equation.

It is important to realise that there are two crucial differences between the effects of ionising radiation, which have been ascribed to the induced DNA double strand breaks, and the UV induced effects, which are ascribed to the pairs of dimers blocking replication.

One difference is that, while one photon of **ionising** radiation can create a 'primary' double strand break in the DNA molecule, a **single UV photon** cannot induce more than a single dimer on one strand of the DNA molecule. This means that, contrary to the case of ionising radiation, there is not a linear slope of effect proportional with UV exposure at low exposures and, as a result, there is virtually no risk of harm at low exposures of UV light.

133

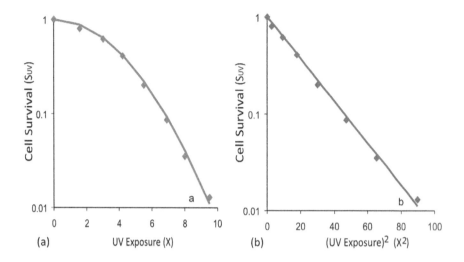

Figure 10.6 *(a) A graphical representation of cell survival data drawn as a function of UV exposure (X). The red line is in accordance with the red equation and the red diamonds are experimental data in mouse cells; (b) the same experimental data (magenta diamonds) drawn as a function of the square of the UV exposure (X²). The straight magenta line is also in accordance with the red equation for cell survival. Note that cell survival is drawn on a logarithmic scale to unravel the exponential equation.*

The other difference is that, although a 'secondary' double strand break is formed immediately during the ionising radiation exposure, the two dimers, induced by two separate UV photons, exist as independent single strand DNA damages and are only recognised as a potential lesion when the DNA replication process starts and the two approaching replication forks are blocked. This means that, whereas a 'secondary' double strand break induced by ionising radiation is recognised immediately as a crucial lesion, the two independent dimers induced by UV photons are not. So, a G_2 cell exposed to UV will pass through mitosis and the next G_1 phase before, in the S phase, any remaining paired dimers between two approaching replication forks would block replication and be recognised as a crucial lesion.

Prof Dee and Dr Hay's Take Home Message is:

UV cell killing might look the same as that from ionising radiation but it isn't. It is not possible for one UV photon to affect both strands of the DNA and so there is no ("A") value, no initial linear slope to the effect curve and little risk of harm at low exposures. And the paired-dimer lesion is not recognised immediately it is formed but, only when it blocks the replication process at the following DNA synthesis cell phase.

Now, you will remember from chapter 6 that, if the exposure time to ionising radiation were extended, the 'first' single strand break could be repaired before the 'second' single strand break occurred to create a double strand break. This would lead to a reduction in the number of 'secondary' double strand breaks with a consequent reduction in the ionising radiation effect. This "dose-rate" effect does not happen with UV exposure because the repair of the dimers is much slower than the repair of single strand breaks. More importantly, it is because each of the two dimers, that might form a crucial lesion, can be independently repaired and this repair can take place both during the UV exposure and all the time after the UV exposure, until the cell moves into the next DNA replication process.

However, in UV exposed, non-dividing, stationary cells, all of the dimers could be perfectly repaired as single strand lesions, given sufficient time, and no paired-dimer lesions would remain when the stationary cells eventually commenced DNA replication. In this case, the UV exposure would have no observable biological effect. Indeed, there are experimental data on cell killing which support this reasoning.

Dr Hay and Prof Dee's Take Home Message is:

Because stationary cells would have a long time to repair the dimers induced by UV exposure, it is reasonable to expect that there would not be any remaining paired-dimer lesions to cause a biological effect when the stationary cells finally move into the cell cycle to replicate their DNA.

It is important to keep in mind that, as with ionising radiation, UV exposure is capable of causing mutations as well as cell killing and that mutations can lead to cancer, in this case, skin cancer. Two of the three types of skin cancer, basal cell and squamous cell carcinoma, are associated with UV exposure of the skin. The third and most dangerous type of skin cancer, malignant melanoma, is less closely associated with UV exposure.

UV exposure does not really induce chromosomal aberrations because the formation of these depends on the repairing of a broken DNA double helix and UV rarely causes breaks in the chromosomes.

10.4 Sunbathing and Sunburn

Figure 10.6 illustrates that UV exposure can cause cell killing and, by association also induce mutations but, what are the connections between these effects and sunbathing?

To get a healthy tan you sunbathe but, if you stay too long in the sun, you get sunburn. Sunburn is a result of excessive cell killing! The skin cells are constantly dying off and being replenished so there is always a slow division of skin cells going on. The slow division of the skin cells means that, after a good sunbathe, the dimers induced by the UV in the sun's rays will have some time to repair but not all will be repaired before some of the skin cells start to replicate their DNA and crucial lesions are recognised. Some of these cells will die so that, a few hours after a good sunbathe, your skin will redden and, if you have been in the sun for too long, this reddening will get worse as more cells die and you get sunburnt. Accompanying this cell killing are, of course, mutations and an increased chance of getting skin cancer.

If you only have a small exposure to sunshine each day, fewer dimers will be formed and the slowly dividing cells will have a better chance of repairing the dimers before the DNA replication starts. This means that cell killing and the chance for mutations will be much reduced. And if you repeat this exposure each day, then you will gradually acquire a tan but avoid a sunburn. As the tan gets stronger, it also acts as a UV shield in the cells against the induction of dimers so that you can gradually increase your time in the sun. The important message is to sunbathe a little each day and avoid sunburn at all costs. Do not forget that the more intense the sunshine, the shorter the time you should spend exposed sunbathing in it. A longer exposure to a weaker sun will have the same effect as a short exposure to an intense sun.

And the Take Home Message is:

Be happy sunbathers! But, remember, 15 minutes face up and 15 minutes face down in a midday, midsummer, Mediterranean sun is plenty to start with for an unprotected, pale skin.

The use of suntan parlours leads to UVA exposures which might indirectly cause single strand breaks in the DNA and might, therefore, cause some cell killing and eventually mutations. However, as the mechanism by which the UVA exposure causes DNA damage has not been fully elucidated, the only advice that can be given is that one should be prudent in the use of suntan parlours.

10.5   Light, Microwaves and Radio Waves

The photon energy of visible light decreases from about 3eV for blue light to about 1.5eV for red and the energy decreases further down the spectrum of electromagnetic radiations into microwaves and radio waves which have photon energies of a fraction of an electron volt. The energies of these photons are too small to cause any breakage or deformation in the DNA and it seems most unlikely that these radiations can cause any permanent DNA damage or dangerous health effects. Microwaves cause the hydrogen atoms to vibrate in water, biological tissue and plastic molecules and can, in this way, cause a heating process, which is how a microwave oven works.

Of course, if part of your body is heated up to more than 41°C (106°F), your cells lyse or disintegrate and die and you suffer a burn and are hurt. Thermal damage can be caused by very close exposure to strong sources of microwaves and radio waves, such as radar and television and radiotransmitters. Therefore, regulations to restrict exposures and avoid thermal damage have been established by an international body of scientists called the International Commission on Non-Ionising Radiation Protection. Non-thermal exposure does not cause any DNA damage and, therefore, it is unlikely to cause any permanent health effects. This means that, although everyone is exposed to radio waves without realising or noticing it from radio and TV transmissions, wifi and mobile telephones, for example, no one is going to suffer any health problems from this exposure. So, rest assured, excessive use of your mobile phone will not give you a brain tumour!

 Dr Hay and Prof Dee's Take Home Message is:

Be happy again! There is no evidence for non-thermal effects of microwaves or radio waves and we are convinced that these non-ionising radiations do not cause permanent health damage at low level exposures.

10.6 Mutagenic Chemicals

Everyone is exposed to low levels of ionising radiation from natural background radioactivity and from cosmic rays without detecting it and this exposure carries a very small health risk that increases as the exposure level increases. Similarly, everyone is exposed to low levels of non-ionising radiation, such as radio waves, without detecting it but this exposure is harmless and has no health risk attached to it. Everyone is also exposed to small levels of very many chemicals often, but not always, without detecting them. However, some of those chemicals have mutagenic properties and, consequently, might pose a health hazard. Clearly, the chemicals which demonstrate mutagenic properties can attack the DNA in the body's cells in such a way as to damage the genetic integrity of the cell, resulting in both mutations and cell killing.

Some chemicals will react with the DNA to cause damage leading to strand breakage and "imitate" ionising radiation creating DNA double strand breaks. Some chemicals will react with the DNA to cause deformations in the DNA strands and will "imitate" ultraviolet B light causing blocks to DNA replication. And some chemicals will cause "cross links" between the two DNA strands leading to either strand breakage or replication blockage.

One important application of chemicals that cause DNA damage is in chemotherapy for the treatment of cancer where these chemicals are specifically designed to be taken up in, and to kill, rapidly dividing tumour cells. Most of the normal body cells are not dividing and are not affected by chemotherapy but some cells that are in constant division, such as hair cells and the cells lining the stomach, are affected and killed. This leads to loss of hair and sickness, both well-known side-effects of chemotherapy.

However, as with ionising radiation, chemical mutagens can also cause cancer through the induction of mutations in normal body cells. This means that chemical mutagens do have a health risk. Although not all chemical mutagens carry a risk that is directly proportional with exposure level, in the way ionising radiation does with the "primary" DNA double strand break, some chemicals will have this sort of low level risk. And that means that these chemical mutagens must be treated with the same care that is given to our exposure to ionising radiation.

Prof Dee and Dr Hay's Take Home Message is:

Some chemicals that we are exposed to have mutagenic and thus carcinogenic activity. We need to be as careful with these chemicals as we are with ionising radiation!

Rounding Up and Rounding Off

By now, you should be able to distinguish between radiation and radioactivity and be aware that everyone is surrounded by both radioactivity and the radiation from it. You are all exposed continually to very low levels of natural background radiation and even you, yourself, are a little radioactive. You should know that all matter is made up of atoms that are in turn made up of a core of protons and neutrons surrounded by orbiting electrons. The atoms join together to form molecules by sharing their outer valency-electrons and this sharing of valency-electrons creates the molecular bond.

Ionising radiations are able to disrupt and eject the atomic electrons, creating energetic secondary electron tracks and breaking the molecular bonds. Non-ionising radiations are unable to break molecular bonds in this way. X-rays and gamma rays form the very energetic part of the spectrum of electromagnetic radiation which also includes the less energetic ultraviolet and visible light, and the much less energetic infrared radiation, microwaves and radio waves. X-rays and gamma rays are penetrating forms of ionising radiation. Other forms of less penetrating ionising radiations are beta particles, which are energetic electrons, and alpha particles, which are energetic helium nuclei. Although alpha particles can be stopped by a sheet of paper, they are very effective biologically. Another type of ionising radiation comes from fast neutron exposure in the form of energetic recoil protons (hydrogen nuclei). Protons are rather effective biologically but they are not very penetrating, whereas fast neutrons are quite penetrating.

DNA, the long, thread-like, double stranded helix molecule which carries all the genetic information that governs the functioning of all our body cells, resides in the nucleus of those cells in the form of chromosomes. Disruption of the DNA double helix disturbs the mechanical and genetic integrity of the chromosome and can cause genetic changes or mutations in the affected cells. The DNA double helix, with the two strands separated by 2nm, is a regular, three dimensional, target molecule for ionising radiations that are capable of breaking the DNA strands. Ionising radiations have the ability to break both strands of the double helix along a single radiation track creating 'primary' double strand breaks. 'Secondary' double strand breaks can also arise when two single strand breaks in opposite strands of the DNA are in close proximity.

The combination of these two modes of double strand break production means that the dose-effect relationship is a linear-quadratic function of radiation dose ($N = AD + BD^2$). Alpha particles and protons are classified as densely ionising radiations because they have short, straight tracks with very close energy depositions, or ionisations, a few nanometers apart. They are efficient producers of 'primary' double strand breaks because the spacing between ionisations closely coincides with the DNA strand separation. X-rays, gamma rays and beta particles are classified as sparsely ionising radiations because the secondary electron tracks they induce are tortuous and the spacing between ionisation events rarely coincides with the DNA strand separation. They are less efficient producers of 'primary' double strand breaks. However, when these secondary electrons have lost most of their energy, their tracks become denser and more efficient producers of 'primary' double strand breaks. It is important to recognise that a unique feature of **all ionising radiations** is their ability, to a greater or lesser extent, to induce 'primary' double strand breaks. This ability is crucially important for the assessment of risks from ionising radiations. Non-ionising radiations do not have this ability.

The DNA double strand break, which disrupts the mechanical integrity of the chromosome, can be directly related to chromosome damage in the form of chromosomal aberrations as well as to mutations resulting from a disruption in the integrity of the genetic function of the cell. The ability of ionising radiations to cause cell killing is associated with a lethal mutation. In this way, the three cellular effects of radiation, the induction of chromosome aberrations, the induction of mutations and the induction of cell killing, can all be linked to double strand breaks and all are expected to have the typical, linear-quadratic dose-effect relationship. This is borne out by the analysis of experimental data. Indeed, the linear-quadratic dose-effect relationship proves to be ubiquitous in radiation biology.

Densely ionising radiations, such as alpha particles and protons, produce more 'primary' double strand breaks and this is revealed in an essentially linear dose-effect relationship with a large (A) component for each of the cellular effects. The influence of protracting the radiation exposure, especially of sparsely ionising radiations, such as gamma and X-rays, is a decrease in the quadratic (B) component of the dose-effect relationship for each of the three cellular effects. This decrease in (B) is a consequence of the cell's ability, given sufficient time, to repair DNA single strand breaks perfectly during exposure.

The association of DNA double strand breaks with each of the three cellular effects means that direct interrelationships, or correlations, should exist between the cellular effects when measured in the same experiment. The analysis of experimental data has revealed these anticipated correlations and, in some experiments, cell killing has been directly related to the induction of DNA double strand breaks.

Hereditary effects arise as the consequence of a cellular mutation in a reproductive or germ cell and may be revealed in the following or subsequent generations. The low dose, low dose rate risk for hereditary effects is, in accordance with the findings for cellular effects, therefore, expected to be linearly proportional with dose. However, there is a lack of data for the occurrence of radiation-induced hereditary effects in humans.

The short-term, or acute, health effects, such as sickness and vomiting, skin burns, anaemia and ultimately death, are caused by relatively large radiation exposures and result from massive cell killing which impairs normal organ functions. The health effects arise soon after exposure when a certain proportion of stem cells are killed, preventing the continued function of a body organ or, in the case of death, the continued function of the organism itself. The dose-effect relationships for these health effects show a typical, long threshold of dose, with no apparent effect, followed by a rapid decrease in the organ or organism's ability to recover a normal function. These dose-effect relationships can be related quantitatively to single cell killing. Consequently, the typical influence of radiation types and protracted exposure on these short-term health effects can also be traced back to the effects occurring at the cellular level. It is often not appreciated that, although no health effect is apparent at exposures within the threshold dose region, substantial cell killing (more than 90%) is, nevertheless, going on.

The induction of cancer is the important late health effect of radiation exposure and may occur at any time from a few to many years after exposure. Radiation-induced cancer arises from a somatic mutation in normal body cells and the dose-effect relationship rises as a linear-quadratic function of increasing dose to pass through a maximum and then decrease at higher doses where cell killing dominates. The dose-effect relationship is quantitatively described by a combination of an equation for mutation induction and an equation for cell survival. The cell mutated to a malignant state must survive to express that malignancy. Experimental data for cancer induction in animals, which reveal the same peak-height induction of cancer, irrespective of the radiation types used, provide convincing evidence for the association of cancer induction with a somatic mutation. The dose-effect relationships reveal the typical influence of radiation types and protraction of radiation exposure. The linear dose-effect relationship for cancer induction caused by protracted exposure to sparsely ionising radiations is crucially important because this forms the basis for the derivation of radiation risk to the general population.

Recommendations based on a comprehensive philosophy for the protection of man from radiation have been developed for many years by the International Commission on Radiological Protection (ICRP). The recommendations are based on the principle that exposures should always be "as low as readily achievable" (ALARA) and are accepted and implemented everywhere in the world. The ICRP's recommended level of radiation risk for sparsely ionising radiations is derived from an analysis of the induction of leukaemia in the atomic bomb survivors. It differs from the analysis adopted here which indicates a lower level of risk for protracted exposures than that recommended by ICRP. However, both

143

analytical methods agree that the dose-effect relationship for protracted exposures to sparsely ionising radiations increases linearly with radiation dose from zero dose up, the linear no-threshold concept.

The mechanistic analysis used here identifies the 'primary' DNA double strand break as the origin of the radiation risk. This predicts that the risk of exposures to the mix of sparsely ionising radiations normally experienced by the public would be larger than that derived from the atomic bomb survivors who were exposed to very energetic gamma rays. Consequently, it is accepted here that the level of risk for cancer induction by protracted exposures of sparsely ionising radiations of 4% per sievert, as proposed by the ICRP, is useful and has stood the test of time.

Everyone is exposed to natural background radiation from radioactivity in the air, soil and water around us and also to cosmic radiation from outer space. Those living in houses built on granite may be exposed to radon gas and its radioactive daughters. Granite contains small amounts of uranium-238 and radon gas is one element in the uranium decay chain. The gas leaks from cracks in the granite and the decay products of radon can attach to dust particles in the air. In homes built on granite, this can lead to an increased exposure of the lungs of the occupants to alpha particle radiation. Techniques to reduce the levels of radon exposure in vulnerable homes have been developed to ensure that the exposure is as low as readily achievable.

The exposure of workers in the radiation industry and radiographers and radiologists in hospitals is closely measured and their monthly, as well as annual, exposures are strictly limited.

Non-ionising radiations such as visible light, infrared light, microwaves and radio waves do not have sufficient energy to damage the DNA molecules, so these radiations are unlikely to cause any permanent harm or health hazard, unless excessive heating of the body occurs. Consequently, exposures to these non-ionising radiations should be kept to levels that avoid heating the body cells.

However, ultraviolet B radiation, which is found in sunlight, does cause damage to the DNA in the form of single strand deformations called dimers. A single UV photon is unable to damage both strands of the DNA. These single strand dimers can be slowly repaired but can block the progress of a DNA replication fork during DNA synthesis. If two dimers, on opposite strands of the DNA molecule, block the progress of two converging replication forks, then they block the replication process and form a potentially lethal lesion. Accordingly, the cell killing effect of UVB radiation is expected to be directly related to the square of the UVB exposure and analysis of data bears this out. In contrast to the case of ionising radiations, where the DNA double strand break is induced immediately, the UVB induced cell killing lesion is only recognised when the cell starts to replicate its DNA. This means that the dimers can be repaired as single stranded damage, both during and after exposure, up to the start of replication. Consequently, stationary cells are able to repair all the dimers, and low levels of exposure to UVB should not cause a health hazard. Unfortunately, skin cells divide slowly so that excessive exposures to UVB, as in long and intensive sunbathing, can cause massive skin cell killing which reveals itself in the form of sunburn. The induction of skin cancer is also a health hazard arising from too much exposure to the UVB in sunlight. It is, therefore, prudent to control sunbathing in order to avoid causing sunburn.

Some of the chemicals which surround us have mutagenic properties and are potentially carcinogenic. These chemicals can pose a health hazard and exposure to them should be treated with the same sort of care that is given to our exposure to ionising radiation.

Summarizing:

Non-ionising radiations are not hazardous at low exposure levels but be aware of the potential health hazard from some mutagenic chemicals.

UVB in sunlight can cause DNA damage which, as a result of massive skin cell killing, leads to sunburn and, as a result of mutation, eventually to skin cancer. But you can avoid these hazards by prudent control of your sunbathing regimes.

Ionising radiations cause double strand breaks in the DNA which lead to cell killing, chromosomal damage and mutations. You are always surrounded by very low levels of ionising radiation which are not a health hazard. You are extremely unlikely to meet large radiation exposures which can cause short-term health hazards, such as radiation sickness. The important health hazard from ionising radiation exposure is the induction of cancer many years later but, although the risk for this increases with each exposure, compared with the normal chance of getting cancer, the risk of getting a radiation-induced cancer is very small.

So, our parting shot is:

Understanding radiation and its effects is the key to living with it without fear!

Bibliography

It is a pleasure to acknowledge that the data presented in figures from chapters 5, 6, 7, 8, 9 and 10 were originally published in the following scientific papers:

Coggle J E, (1988) Lung tumour induction in mice after x-rays and neutrons. *International Journal of Radiation Biology*, volume **53**, pages 585-598. (see Figure 8.3)

Dewey W C, Furman S C and Miller H H, (1970) Comparison of lethality and chromosomal damage induced by X-rays in synchronized Chinese hamster cells *in vitro*. *Radiation Research*, volume **43**, pages 561-581. (see Figure 6.15)

Dewey W C, Stone L E, Miller H H and Giblak R E, (1971a) Radiosensitization with 5-bromo-deoxyuridine of Chinese hamster cells irradiated during different phases of the cell cycle. *Radiation Research*, volume **47**, pages 672-688. (see Figure 6.15)

Dewey W C, Miller H H and Leeper D B, (1971b) Chromosomal aberrations and mortality of X-irradiated mammalian cells; emphasis on repair. *Proceedings of the National Academy of Science USA*, volume **68**, pages 667-671. (see Figure 6.15)

Hornsey S, (1973) The effectiveness of fast neutrons compared with low LET radiation on cell survival measured in the mouse jejunum. *Radiation Research*, volume 55, pages 58-68. (see Figure 7.6)

Iliakis G and Nusse M, (1982) Conditions supporting repair of potentially lethal damage causes a significant reduction of ultraviolet-induced division delay in synchronized and plateau-phase Erlich Ascites Tumor cells. *Radiation Research*, volume **91**, pages 483-506. (see Figure 10.6)

Leenhouts H P, Sijsma M J, Cebulska-Wasilewska A and Chadwick K H, (1986) The combined effect of DBE and X-rays on the induction of somatic mutations in Tradescantia. *International Journal of Radiation Biology*, volume **49**, pages 109-119. (see Figure 6.10)

Lloyd D C, Purrott R J, Dolphin G W and Edwards A A, (1976) Chromosome aberrations induced in human lymphocytes by neutron irradiation. *International Journal of Radiation Biology*, volume 29, pages 169-182. (see Figure 6.6)

Lloyd D C, Edwards A A, Prosser J S et al., (1984) The dose response relationship obtained at constant irradiation times for the induction of chromosome aberrations in human lymphocytes by cobalt-60 gamma rays. *Radiation and Environmental Biophysics*, volume **23**, pages 179-189. (see Figures 6.5, 6.6, 6.7)

Major I R and Mole R H, (1978) Myeloid leukaemia in X-ray irradiated CBA mice. *Nature*, volume **272**, page 455. (see Figures 8.4, 8.5)

Metting N F, Braby L A, Roesch W C et al., (1985) Dose-rate evidence for two kinds of radiation damage in stationary-phase mammalian cells. *Radiation Research*, volume **103**, pages 204-212. (see Figures 6.12, 6.14)

Mole R H, Papworth D G and Corp M J, (1983) The dose-response for x-ray induction of myeloid leukaemia in male CBA/H mice. *British Journal of Cancer*, volume **47**, pages 285-291. (see Figures 8.4, 8.5)

Mole R H and Davids J A G, (1982) Induction of myeloid leukaemia and other tumours in mice by irradiation with fission neutrons. In "Neutron Carcinogenesis" (Eds. J Broerse & G Gerber) (CEC, Luxemburg) page 31. (see Figures 8.4, 8.6)

Murray D, Prager A and Milas L, (1989) Radioprotection of cultured mammalian cells by amniothiols WR-1065 and WR-255591: correlation between protection against DNA double-strand breaks and cell killing after γ-radiation. *Radiation Research*, volume **120**, pages 154-163. (see Figures 5.7, 6.17)

Pierce D A, Shimizu Y, Preston D L, Vaeth M and Mabuchi K, (1996) Studies of the mortality of atomic bomb survivors, report 12, part 1, Cancer 1950 – 1990. *Radiation Research*, volume **146**, pages 1-27. (see Figures 9.1, 9.2, 9.3)

Rao B S and Hopwood L E, (1982) Modification of mutation frequency in plateau Chinese hamster ovary cells exposed to gamma radiation during recovery from potentially lethal damage. *International Journal of Radiation Biology*, volume **42**, pages 501-508. (see Figure 6.16)

Richold M and Holt P D, (1974) The effect of differing neutron energies on mutagenesis in cultured Chinese hamster cells. In: "Biological effects of Neutron Irradiation" (IAEA, Vienna) pages 237-244. (see Figures 6.8, 6.9, 6.13)

Traynor J E and Still E T, (1968) Dose rate effect on LD50/30 in mice exposed to cobalt-60 gamma irradiation. Brooks Air Force Base, TX:USAF School of Aerospace Medicine; Rep. SAM-TR-68-97. (see Figures 7.2, 7.6, 7.9)

Upton A C, Jenkins V K and Conklin J W, (1964) Myeloid leukemia in the mouse. *Annals of the New York Academy of Science*, volume **114**, pages 189-202. (see Figure 8.2)

The paper on DNA double strand break repair, which inspired the approach to chromosome aberrations, was:

Resnick M A, (1976) The repair of double-strand breaks in DNA: A model involving recombination. *Journal of Theoretical Biology*, volume **59**, pages 97-106. (see Figure 6.3)

And the papers on UV induced replication blocking, which inspired the work on UV effects, were:

Cleaver J E, (1981) Inhibition of DNA replication by hydroxyurea and caffeine in an ultraviolet-irradiated human fibroblast cell line. *Mutation Research,* volume **82,** pages 159-171. (see Figures 10.3, 10.4)

Cleaver J E, Thomas G H and Park S D, (1979) Xeroderma pigmentosum variants have slow recovery of DNA synthesis after irradiation with ultraviolet light. *Biochimica Biophysica Acta,* volume **564,** pages 122-131. (see Figures 10.3, 10.4)

Park S D and Cleaver J E, (1979a) Post replication repair: questions of its definition and possible alteration in xeroderma pigmentosum cell strains. *Proceedings of the National Academy of Science USA,* volume **76,** pages 3927-3931. (see Figures 10.3, 10.4)

Park S D and Cleaver J E, (1979b) Recovery of DNA synthesis after ultraviolet irradiation of xeroderma pigmentosum cells depends on excision repair and is blocked by caffeine. *Nucleic Acid Research,* volume **6,** pages 1151-1159. (see Figures 10.3, 10.4)

Acknowledgements

I wish to thank Glenys Marriott for putting me in touch with York Publishing Services. I am pleased to express my appreciation of the sheer professionalism shown by Duncan Beal, Clare Brayshaw and all the staff at York Publishing Services during the preparation of this book. Without their help, advice and expertise it would not have come to fruition. It has been a pleasure to work with them.

Ken Chadwick

Kendal

June 2014